LIFE in a RIDE

Stories of a Son, Actor and L.A. Uber Driver

MARK BLOOM

ISBN: 978-1-7334901-0-8 (Paperback)
ISBN: 978-1-7334901-1-5 (Hardback)
ISBN: 978-1-7334901-2-2 (E-BOOK)

Events in this book are from the author's memory and perspective. Certain names and identifying characteristics have been changed.

LifeInARide@gmail.com

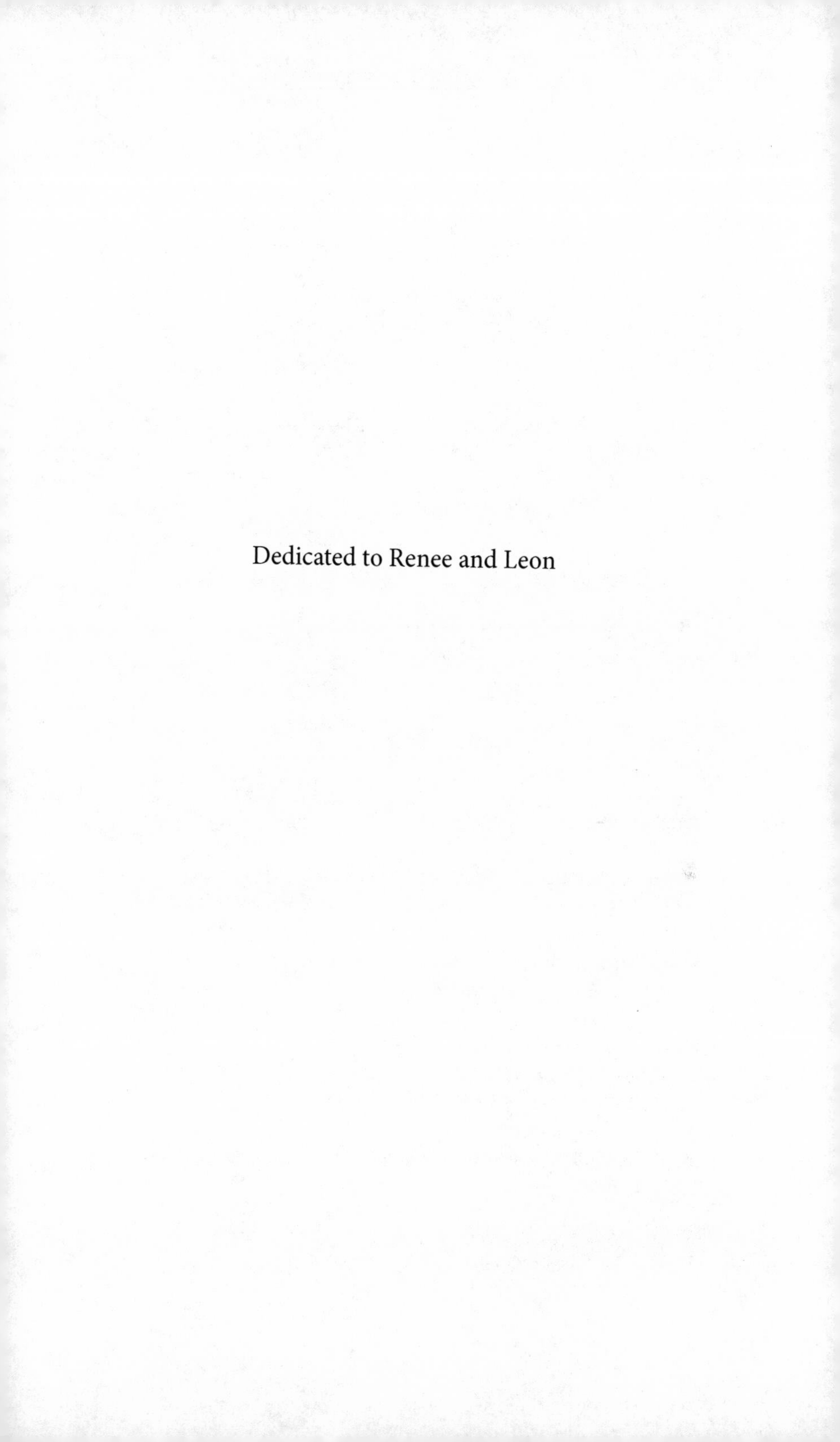

Dedicated to Renee and Leon

"FIREBALL"
(AN INTRODUCTION)

I often find that people aren't aware of their own traits. They meander through life, questioning why their path is going a certain direction, never thinking to look in the mirror where many answers lie. Admittedly, I've done the same. But there's one thing I've always been cognizant of: I'm a sensitive person. I came out of the womb crying and haven't stopped since. Anything that stirs emotions—funerals, weddings, a sappy television commercial—can release the waterworks, leaving me bawling for minutes on end.

And I hate it. I hate being so sensitive. I find it to be a sign of weakness.

Furthering my displeasure, crying has often left me feeling ashamed to the point of self-loathing...*You're not strong enough! Toughen up!*...My pep talks have never helped.

When I was a young boy, no one garnered more pleasure from my sensitivity than my two older brothers, who reveled in how easily they could get me to weep—it's what older brothers do. Their assault tactics were always by verbal provocation. Physically putting me in my place was never a challenge for them, so they'd torture me with words. Tears would explode from my eyes, snot would shoot from my nose, and they'd crown themselves "the best teasers in all the land."

But despite my sensitivity, I was also confident during my early years. I was well ahead of my classmates at school, I was one of the better athletes, and I was adventurous.

My family lived in a house high above Los Angeles in the mythical hills of Laurel Canyon. It's where hippies, freethinkers, and young, bright professionals lived. The community was also well known for drug use and swingers, but I—of course—was far too young to know of such activities. However, the lifestyle of being a free spirit, thinking outside the box, and living life as one wants to was not foreign to my mindset.

When I was six, my parents went on a trip to Israel, leaving my brothers and me with our grandmother. She didn't drive and hanging around the house day after day soon became boring. So, one day I left the house unannounced and walked far down our narrow, winding street to the local elementary school to seek out some friends. I couldn't find anyone, and with no other ideas in mind, I trudged back up the steep hill, arriving home three hours after my excursion began. There I found my panicked grandma.

GRANDMA: Where have you been?!
ME: I went for a walk. It's boring here.

She wasn't pleased—rightfully so—and her reaction became one of the first realizations I had that my free-living ways could have consequences.

GRANDMA: You could have been kidnapped, run over by a car, *killed!*

I said nothing in return, but her words began the erosion of my confidence and adventurous spirit.

When I was seven, we moved from Laurel Canyon to the San Fernando Valley, where any remnants of that confident kid were forever washed away. My entire being changed. Along with being sensitive, I became moody, angry, and quiet. I'm not sure why I changed so dramatically, but something happened, and it turned the dial.

It didn't help that my father traveled a great deal for work, leaving my mom at home to deal with three very different and difficult sons. My relationship with her was fine but never super close. We didn't have similar interests and communication was always an issue. Quite possibly the biggest "gift" she gave me was showing me how to be a worrier. I know all moms worry, but if worrying was a sport, my mom would be a ten-time all-star and first-ballot hall of fame inductee.

I adhered to the characteristic and became further introverted. I'd sit alone in my room for hours at a time and study the backs of baseball cards or erect Rube Goldberg contraptions that I called "marble machines." And while I always had a best friend and played with the neighborhood kids, it scared me to reach out to other children, thinking they wouldn't find me worthy of their companionship.

Along with staying in my room, I found three other ways to compensate for my self-doubt. First, even at a very early age, I had good comedic timing. Getting a room full of kids to laugh was a rush, and it gave me some stature at school. But truthfully—like many comedians—I was hiding behind the jokes and laughter to shield my insecurities, and by the time I'd get home from school

I would revert to the quiet, timid kid who didn't think anyone liked him.

My second outlet was sports. My next-door neighbor, Mike, and I would shoot hoops, pitch tennis balls to one another, and throw a football around all day, but if he wasn't home, I'd stay sequestered in my room.

Team sports weren't a great match for me either. I'd put tremendous pressure on myself to not let others down and not to look foolish. By the end of most games, I was crying again, especially in baseball (I was a terrible pitcher). Eventually, I gravitated to individual sports: first bowling, then karate—which I ended up practicing and teaching for over twenty-five years—so that any success or failure landed squarely on my shoulders. Unfortunately, I still cried a lot.

Only when I got to high school did I try team sports again. I played "Bee Basketball" my junior and senior years and was named captain both seasons (mostly because I'd dive after loose balls and take charges, not because I was a big vocal leader). The two seasons were very enjoyable, however, and some of the stone that had surrounded me for so long got chipped away, allowing tiny hints of my old self to occasionally resurface.

My final outlet was pinball. We lived down the street from a bowling alley where there was a set of ever-revolving machines. I was good and could master most games within a few days, but one always gave me fits. The machine was named *Fireball,* and it had one unique quality: In the middle of the board—between the top bumpers and the flippers down below—sat a red circle. Most of the time, the circle literally did nothing and had no effect on the game, but when prompted by hitting the wrong bumper or something of the sort, it would light up and transform into a spinning wheel—*the fireball.* From there, whenever the pinball crossed its path, the fireball would dramatically change its course, slinging it to wherever the arcade gods desired.

The machine aggravated me to no end. I couldn't control it, and the fortunes of the game changed too quickly for my liking. There I'd be: knocking down all the right targets, registering points like a character out of a rock-and-roll song, and suddenly—randomly—the fireball would shoot the pinball right between the flippers or down one of the side chutes to finish a play... *Well, damn!*

I think life can be like that: a particular event, a moment in time that dramatically changes our journey, causing us to spin off to who-knows-where. It *can* happen. But such pronounced shifts usually take place in our youth. As kids, we are balls of clay, easily shaped and transformed by our experiences and the people surrounding us. The older we get, however, the more we become solidified in our actions, thoughts, and routines, leading to predictable steps. Sure, there can be significant life-changing moments as an adult—meeting the love of one's life, the sudden passing of a friend—but mostly we become creatures of habit. In fact, changes are often so minuscule and overlooked that the only true way to recognize our transformations is by stepping outside ourselves. From that vantage point, we can view the paths we have taken and gain an honest perspective as to who we had been and who we are now. Then, and only then—*by viewing ourselves as an outsider might*—can we truly recognize the person we've become and the gradual changes we have made...

Take Mark, for instance: a single guy who was once an aspiring actor. *Once.* Now at the ripe age of 49, he is still an actor, but no longer does he think of himself as "aspiring" (he believes that definition is intended for those two to three decades younger than he). Instead, he prefers to think of himself as a "surviving actor."

His life has been this way for decades. Ever since college, he has been steadily pursuing a creative outlet to be his profession. From doing stand-up comedy to writing children stories (and everything in between), he's been driven to be an "artist." But as is often the case with an artist's journey, his life—especially when it comes to finances—hasn't always been easy.

However, with his 50th birthday closing fast, there seems to be a glimmer of hope that's getting brighter by the day: The surviving actor is experiencing the best stretch of his career. During the first five months of 2016, he's booked roles on six TV shows, including *Silicon Valley* and *Black-ish,* and has just finished shooting an independent movie, *School Spirits*, in St. Joseph, Missouri. The film is an eye-opening experience for him. The director is terrific, the cast and crew are friendly and enthusiastic, and the character he plays has some depth to it, unlike many roles he auditions for, which can be as simple as a single line of dialogue that moves the story along. It's the type of work he's longed for...*If I could consistently book jobs like this, I'd be a very happy man.*

But despite these successes, he still struggles to cover his bills. Much of that has to do with how the Hollywood landscape has changed: Movie stars are now accepting television roles, which is pushing everyday, ordinary actors down a rung while pushing money to the top. Meanwhile, the commercial world is in no better shape as many productions have gone non-union. These shifts have essentially killed off a once-thriving middle class of performers and have forced almost everyone to find multiple income sources. Mark is no different. Along with pursuing acting, he also works as a headshot photographer, and he coaches high school basketball at a private school. Luckily, the rent-controlled apartment he lives in deflects much of the high cost of Los Angeles living.

But then, to his utter dismay, the worst neighbors of all time move in next door. It's a couple: she is a bartender, and he?—Well Mark isn't sure, but he believes his new neighbor either wants to be a DJ or a rapper. Either way, it means Earth-shattering, bass-driven music pulsates into his apartment throughout the day. Then, at two in the morning, the girlfriend comes home, wired from her bartending job, and watches action movies for hours on end. All attempts to speak with them are met with scoffs and "deal with it" responses.

Adding to the problem is the fact that Mark's landlord *wants* him to move, so she's not bound by rent-control and can significantly raise the price of the apartment the moment he walks out the door. Complaining is deemed useless; he succumbs to searching for another place to live and an inevitable increase in rent.

The search isn't easy; even when he finds a suitable place, his profession often gets in the way.

LANDLORD: Your income is too unpredictable. Sorry, I don't rent to actors.
MARK: But I've been on six shows this year. You look like you watch *Silicon Valley*. Do you like *Silicon Valley?*
LANDLORD: Sorry.

For two months he scours L.A. neighborhoods before finally finding a terrific apartment in North Hollywood. Initially, moving from the Westside back to "the Valley" isn't very appetizing to him, but the building is well kept, there's a large balcony attached to the apartment, and—most importantly—his neighbors are quiet. There's also one more advantage: The move brings him closer to his mom.

Two and a half years earlier, Mark's dad passed away. Soon thereafter, his mom moved from San Diego to nearby Thousand Oaks. Now eighty-one and with declining health, she's living with her middle son, so he can concentrate on his business while she watches over his young daughter. It's not the most ideal situation, but it's working out, and Mark's happy to visit her whenever possible.

The positives to his move far outweigh the negatives, but he still has one question...*How am I going to afford a $400 rent increase?*

The answer is easy: He begins driving for Uber. He can cover his bills by driving as much as is needed, and the flexibility of when he works is perfect for acting.

Like any new undertaking, it takes a little while for him to get adjusted, but the more he drives, the more he finds the job to be quite fascinating. For one thing—like all Uber drivers—the eventual destination is unknown until he picks up the passenger and *then* swipes the app. While some trips funnel into the death-grip that is L.A. traffic, others lead to interesting neighborhoods he's never explored or to scenic overlooks of the downtown skyline.

Then, one day, he has a much bigger realization: Every ride is like a one-act play. The passenger gets in the car, the door is shut, the app is swiped, and suddenly he and a complete stranger are in a confined, intimate space. Many encounters are simply snippets of the rider's day while others run much deeper: stories are told, secrets are revealed, there are clashes and unexpected bonds. He witnesses slices of life so profound, and delves so deeply into the human condition, that he has to pull over to regroup once he's dropped of the passenger.

Every genre is explored in the rolling theater: tragedies, dramas, comedies of the absurd. Each rider has their own unique story and interactions can go any of a million directions...*I feel like I've landed on the fireball*...He meets people he'd never get to meet otherwise, learns by listening to other's perspectives, and occasionally even shares some of his own wisdom, especially to younger passengers.

And then—just as quickly as it had begun—the curtain falls, and the trip is over. The passenger exits, Mark pulls away, and each character goes their separate way, most likely never to cross paths again.

For the rider, it's time to move about their day. For Mark, he waits for the app to chime once more, signaling the beginning of his next adventure and the next life in a ride...

"To me, there are three things we should all do every day....
Number 1 is laugh. You should laugh every day.
Number 2 is think. You should spend some time in thought.
Number 3 is you should have your emotions moved to tears....
Think about it. If you laugh, you think, and you cry,
that's a full day. That's a heck of a day."
—Jim Valvano

- 2016 -

“FINDING YOUR PLACE IN A HAPPY SPACE”

It’s 6:30 on a Friday night. Mark is parked on a quiet residential street in Sherman Oaks. He waits patiently for his passenger, *Bill.*

A few moments pass when from a modest house out bounds a boy in his late teens. A bit awkward but with pep to his step, he gets to the car and sits in the passenger seat.

MARK: Hi, Bill. How are you doing?
TEENAGER: “Bill” is actually my dad. I’m Steven.
MARK: Oh, gotcha. How are you doing, Steven?
STEVEN: I’m great!

And that he is.

It doesn’t take a decorated detective to discover that Steven loves life. His enthusiasm, demeanor, and unending energy is infectious, and soon Mark is smiling as well. Truth be told—and there’s really no other way to put it—Steven is a Super Nerd: slim frame, big glasses, an overeagerness that could choke a hippo. And the beautiful thing?—He could not care less.

MARK: So, where are you heading to?
STEVEN: To my high school’s homecoming game.
MARK: Nice.

STEVEN: Yeah, I think we've got a really great team. We should do well tonight.

Mark's smile grows as he thinks back to his high school days and football games.

MARK: Do you go to all the games?
STEVEN: Oh yeah. Me and my friends go. It's fun.

The Uber App shows that Steven's destination is the highly regarded private school, Harvard/Westlake.

MARK: You go to Harvard, huh?
STEVEN: I sure do!
MARK: How's your experience been?

He waits for the shoe to drop. Somewhere along the way Steven must have been bullied, got tied to a goal post, or sat alone at lunch for weeks at a time.

STEVEN: Oh, it's been fantastic. I've met so many great people. My friends and I have a great time whatever we do.

Steven continues speaking with tremendous fervor as he lists the activities he's involved in and the colleges he's applying to.

Mark is engrossed, but then he falls into the trap: the "If I knew then what I know now" trap...*Man, high school could have been so much better.*

He quickly snaps out of his thought pattern, however, and glances over to see his wide-eyed passenger grinning from ear to ear. He's thrilled for Steven: a kid who has found his place and is enjoying every minute...*He's gonna have a great life.*

As they arrive, Steven can't unbuckle his seatbelt fast enough.

STEVEN: Thanks for the ride.
MARK: You're welcome. Have a great time tonight.

Steven turns as he exits; a smile plasters his face.

STEVEN: I will!

Mark pulls away and slowly nods...*Yes, you will, Steven. Yes, you will.*

"HELPLESS"

Mark is driving around Hollywood on a drizzly night. A request comes in from *Carissa.*

As is often the case, the unreliable Uber GPS directs him to an empty alley...*Dammit, Uber*...He idles for a moment and does a 360 scan of the area: No Carissa. He shakes his head, mutters obscenities at the app, and calls her.

CARISSA: Hel-lo.
MARK: Hey, Carissa, it's your Uber driver. I'm trying to find your location.
CARISSA: I-am-st-a-and-ing-i-in-front-of-Pi-inks.

He hesitates for a moment.

MARK: Um, okay. Just give me a second. I'll be right there.
CARISSA: Tha-anks.

He drives out of the alley and slowly makes his way in front of the legendary hot dog stand, Pinks. There, he spots Carissa. Her head is down, her shoulders are slumped. The only part of her standing upright is her big, beautiful hair, which is glistening from the moisture in the air. She gets in the backseat, shuts the door, and immediately begins sobbing.

Mark twists to her. Tears are flowing down her face...*Oh shoot!...* Quickly he rotates back and swipes the app. As he waits for traffic to clear, he glances in the rearview mirror. His mind spins in an attempt to find words that will soothe her, but he finds nothing in his search. Instead, he sits silently—helplessly—as Carissa's chest heaves.

What if she's in some sort of trouble? What if she needs to get to the police or go to the hospital? Dammit, this was not in the online instructional video...Say something. Say something.

MARK: Um, are you okay, Carissa? Is there anything I can do for you?
CARISSA: (almost apologetically) No-o.

Reluctantly, he nods...*Maybe someone died. This is exactly how you cried when Dad passed.*

They ride in silence for the next few minutes before pulling up to her destination.

MARK: Um...I hope your night gets better.
CARISSA: Tha-anks.

She steps into the cool night; the drizzle mocks her falling tears. Mark watches her slowly—painfully—make her way forward; her shoulders convulsing with every step. She disappears into the shadows, the last visible image being her glistening hair—still standing strong and proud.

A feeling of inadequacy fills Mark's body. He slumps...*You did what you could. You did what you could.*

For a few moments guilt weighs him down, making it near impossible for him to move. But soon the app chimes; a new request has been made. He sits taller, takes in a deep breath, swipes to see the pickup address, and drives on…

"EMO-GEE, WHY DID I DO THAT?!"

Mark is driving near LAX in the midst of a "pool." A pool is when multiple passengers share a trip. It's a little cheaper for the riders but can often leave them unruly because of the added time, which can be extensive if there's multiple pick-ups and drops.

On this occasion the car is already full: A woman is occupying the front seat; a couple is in the back. Traffic is heavy, everyone is quiet, and each rider is looking down at their cellphones.

They pull up to a red light.

As they wait, Mark gets a text from a childhood friend—*Chuckie.*

MARK: Hey, guys, do you mind if I answer my friend's text during the red?
PASSENGERS: No...No...Nope.

Hurriedly he texts Chuckie, letting him know that he's free for lunch the following afternoon, all the while giving his passengers play-by-play details.

MARK: Old buddy...Recently ran into each other...Trying to make plans.

Just as the light turns green, Chuckie texts back: Tomorrow is good for him as well.

Mark prompts his emoji favorites page, hits "thumbs up", presses send, and begins driving. Seconds later, he glances at his phone.

MARK: What the heck?...Oh, no, no, no!
FRONT SEAT: What's wrong?
MARK: I hit the "kissy face" emoji!
FRONT SEAT: Wait! What?
MARK: I meant to hit "thumbs up," but I sent him a "kissy face" by mistake.

ALL—OUT—LAUGHTER!

MARK: No, you don't get it: This guy was the star athlete, tough guy. I haven't seen him in years. I can't send him kissy faces!

The howls of laughter rise to an even higher level.

They stop at another red light. Mark stares at the text. Chuckie hasn't responded.

MARK: What do I do? (the light turns green) *Shit!*
FRONT SEAT: Do you want me to text him while you're driving? I could tell him you meant to hit "thumbs up."

He thinks about her plan.

MARK: No, the pause was too long; it'll seem even worse, like I was trying to cover it up. I'll just have to explain it to him tomorrow.

For the next five minutes all three passengers can't stop laughing. The couple is literally in tears.

They arrive at the first drop-off. The woman in the front seat begins exiting, but before closing the door, she spins to Mark, puckers and winks. Another explosion of laughter erupts from the backseat.

FRONT SEAT: Enjoy your lunch.

Mark nods and gulps... *This is going to be one heck of an interesting reunion.*

(* Actual Passenger Feedback.
** Feedback not necessarily in congruence with corresponding stories)

"AFTER MIDNIGHT"

In the short time Mark's been driving one thing has become quite apparent: He will not drive late at night on Fridays and Saturdays when people are making their way home from bars. Despite price "surges" and the opportunity to make much more money during those hours, it only takes a few exasperating trips to know that drunk passengers are often horrible passengers: they're obnoxious…and loud…and inconsiderate. Plus, Mark knows himself all too well: rude, self-centered people—an L.A. staple—do not mix well with his mercurial temper. He just wants people to be considerate… *Is that really asking too much?*…Unfortunately, drunks rarely appease his wishes.

But as he heads home on a *Tuesday* at 12:30 AM, he's had no such problems. It's been a productive night: plenty of trips, some nice conversations, a decent amount of money's been made. The evening's results have put him in a good mood, *and* he's looking forward to an audition scheduled for the next day. It's not a big role—a couple of lines for a new show he knows nothing about—but summer months are notoriously slow, so the two lines look like a pot of gold at the end of a rainbow.

He reaches down to turn off the app, but just before he closes out, another request comes in…*I suppose I can handle one more trip.*

He swipes and sees the pickup location is in Laurel Canyon...*How about that? Back to the old neighborhood.*

As he ascends into the hills, he flashes back to the first house he lived in. Designed by his dad, it was a beautiful, spacious home with large windows that faced easterly. He distinctly remembers his father waking him one morning so he could see an incredible swirling sunrise. The clouds and colors danced so vividly that day, it was as if Mother Nature herself had painted the sky with streaks of rainbow sherbet.

He smiles at the recollection.

After crossing some memory stirring landmarks, he parks and waits. Moments later, a man and woman in their early twenties step up to the car. They slide into the backseat. She is quiet and non-expressive as if designed by a mannequin manufacturer; he is the complete opposite.

MR. ENTHUSIASM: Hey, buddy!!
MARK: Hi.
MR. ENTHUSIASM: I just need to make a drop-off for my boss. Thanks for picking us up!

Immediately red flags rise...*What kind of drop-off does somebody make at 12:30 in the morning? And why is she coming along?*

He looks in the rearview mirror. The woman keeps staring straight ahead...*Fuck. Something does not feel right about this...Dammit! Why did you accept the trip? You know nothing good happens after midnight.*

Half-heartedly, he swipes. The destination is San Clemente—an hour and a half away.

MARK: Oh, I'm sorry, guys, I can't do this trip; it's too far away. I won't get home until three or four, and I've got stuff to do in the morning.
MR. ENTHUSIASM: Oh, okay, I get it. No problem, buddy.

The two begin exiting when suddenly another voice barks out. Mark looks to his left and sees a man—the *boss* most likely—storming towards him.

BOSS: What the fuck is going on?!
MR. ENTHUSIASM: It's okay, it's okay. It's too long of a trip for him to take.
BOSS: What?!!

The boss knocks on Mark's window.

BOSS: Why the fuck did you accept the trip?!
MARK: We don't know the destination until we pick up the passenger.
BOSS: Fuckin' bullshit!

Instinctively, the boss reaches toward his back-belt loop, and as he does so, the climactic scene in every mafia, gangster, and action movie flashes in front of Mark's face...*Ah fuck-Ah fuck-Ah fuck. Punch it. Get the fuck out of here*...He glances in the mirror. The woman is still making her way out of the car...*Fuck! Fuck!*

Mr. Enthusiasm does his best to defuse the situation.

MR. ENTHUSIASM: It's okay, It's okay. We'll find someone who will take the trip…(To Mark) Don't worry. It's okay, buddy.

Mark isn't so sure about that; he keeps staring up at the boss who keeps staring down at him.

Minutes seem to pass when the boss's hand finally reappears from behind his back…empty.

Whew!

With the woman now out of the car, Mr. Enthusiasm pokes his head in.

MR: ENTHUSIASM: Thanks anyway, buddy. Have a good rest of your night.

Mark smiles, then peels out. He rolls through a stop sign, makes a sharp left, and speeds back to the Valley—his heart racing faster than the car itself.

That is definitely not how I remember the old neighborhood. Guess I'll have to find a new spot to see rainbow sherbet sunrises. Sorry about that, Pop.

"Best Uber driver I have seen. Be safe on the road."

"ARE YOU NOT ENTERTAINED?"

It's a mid-week summer evening, and all of L.A. seems to have stayed in for the night. For the last forty-five minutes Mark has been driving around without getting a single request. To make matters worse, he is not in a great place. Geographically he's fine, emotionally he's not. Much of his anxiety is because of the same old stuff: not enough auditions, money is tight, his social life sucks. But he knows that his heightened level of concern has less to do with life's normal stresses and more to do with what had happened over the weekend...

* * *

Mark gets in his car and heads out to see his mom. A few minutes earlier he had called to see if she wanted to go out to dinner. She accepted his invitation but seemed to be in a bit of a malaise... *Probably just the hot weather.*

When he arrives he knocks on the door; there's no answer... *Weird...*He knocks a few more times and the door swings open. She looks tired.

MARK: Hey, are you okay?

She says she's fine, but her speech is slow, jumbled, and slurred. She sits down and has trouble focusing on Mark, who again asks if she's all right. She answers to the affirmative, but her speech pattern is even worse.

He takes no chances and calls 9-1-1.

MOM: I'm okay, I'm okay.
MARK: No, something is wrong.

Turns out they are both correct.

She has Type 2 diabetes, and her blood sugar is low, causing her lethargy. The paramedics give her an IV, and she's quickly back to normal but is taken to the hospital as a precaution. There, they detect a small stroke. The doctors aren't overly concerned, however, and feel a small change in her medication will prevent similar incidents from happening. It's a relief to everyone but another shot of reality. Along with his dad's passing, Mark has also watched his uncle pass as well as a few of his friends' parents. One's mortality has become an ever-increasing train of thought.

...Another twenty minutes pass without a ride request...*I'm not out here for my health, ya know. How about a trip Uber gods?...* The app chimes...*About time.*

He pulls up to a large apartment building and waits. Five minutes drag by without a sign of his passenger, *Chad,* so he calls.

CHAD: Hello?

MARK: Hey, Chad, it's your Uber driver. Just wanted to let you know that I'm here.
CHAD: Oh shoot, have you been waiting long?
MARK: About five minutes.
CHAD: Damn. I'll give them a call.
MARK: You'll give who a call?
CHAD: You're picking up two girls and driving them to my place. I'll let them know you're waiting.
MARK: Oh, okay, thanks.

Five minutes pass. Nothing.

CHAD: Hello?
MARK: Still me Chad.
CHAD: They haven't come out yet?
MARK: Nope. Listen, I'm going to have to cancel the ride. I'm losing money.
CHAD: No-no-no, please-please-please, I promise they'll be out in just a second.

Since it's been slow all evening—and who knows if there will be any other requests—he agrees to wait.

Seven minutes pass. Nothing.

Now Mark's back in his head: he's thinking about his mom, he's thinking about his own life, he's thinking about how rude some people can be. Emotions from all corners of his body begin to mix. He's angry, disillusioned, numb.

Fuck this!

He reaches forward to cancel the trip, but just before striking the app, he looks left, and sure enough, strolling casually down the street, are two women in their early 20s.

He shakes his head, still considers canceling, but knowing he needs the money, he thinks better of it.

The young women get in the car: one in the front seat, one in the back. They offer no apology for making Mark wait. His blood begins to simmer.

FRONT SEAT: Hi!!
MARK: Hi.

He says nothing more, only begins driving up Santa Monica Boulevard towards West Hollywood. However, as they hit red light after red light, tension continues to build within him. He breathes in deeply and sighs through his nose. Less and less is he able to hide his feelings, and with all of life's thoughts circling around his head like a never-ending tornado, his expression becomes listless.

Minutes later, the woman in the front seat giggles. In his periphery, he notices she's texting. The moment she stops typing the woman in the backseat giggles. He realizes that neither woman has spoken for minutes—literally not a word. Instead, they have become a ping pong match of gigglers: text-giggle, wait-giggle, text-giggle.

Are they making fun of me?

He decides to test his theory. As they stop at another red light, he releases an exaggerated sigh. Simultaneously, the girls burst out laughing. The joyous sound—one which has always given Mark great pleasure—instead, unleashes rage within him…*Fuck you two!!! Self- absorbed, egocentric assholes!!! What?! Am I supposed to entertain you?!?*

His hands latch tightly on to the steering wheel...*Fuck you! My mom just had a stroke!!! Can I just drive you to your destination without you making fun of me?!? Can I???*...He writhes...*You want depressed?! Angry?! Fuck yeah, I can give you that!*...His fingers begin turning white...*Do something! Do it!! Do it!!!*

...He does nothing. He simply smothers his rage with every inhale and stores it in the core of his body.

Fuck them. Don't give them the satisfaction of getting to you.

After another five minutes of giggling the woman in the front seat speaks up.

FRONT SEAT: (mockingly) So, how's your day going?

A muffled giggle from the backseat slides into Mark's ears like a pair of serpents.

He turns to the woman up front. He stares at her without a hint of emotion.

MARK: It's been fine. How about you?

The smirk on her face drops ever so slightly...*Got her!*

Acting may not be deemed a highly trained, intelligence-based skill to outsiders, but there's one thing trained actors can always do: pick up on a stimulus. Whether it be a change in one's tone of voice, a tiny facial tick, or a body position adjustment, all cues are registered. After all, "acting is reacting," and if one's not in tune with his or her partner, then the golden moments are missed.

The moment her smile fell he knew she didn't get the response she was expecting.

She quickly looks away.

For the last five minutes of the ride the young women stay quiet. Mark pulls up to their destination. He looks over.

MARK: You have a good night.
FRONT SEAT: Um…yeah…You too.

He leaves with his pride intact, his temper similarly so. His mom still on his mind.

"Great driver! Relaxed and great to chat with. Enjoyed the ride!"

★★★★★

"A TALE OF TWO CITIES"

It's early evening on a Monday. Mark is traveling down the befittingly named street, Avenue of the Stars, to pick up *Jim* near the back gate of the Fox Studio lot. He knows the area well as he has entered that gate many times before while on his way to an audition.

The simple thought of an audition sends fantasies swirling through his head…*I bet Jim's a big-time casting director, looking to cast a big-time role, on a big-time show. We have a great conversation, Jim becomes a fan, and he gives his Super-Duper-Uber Driver—that's me!—a shot at it. I kill the audition, book the part, and I never have to hear the words, "In 400 feet, pick up Martin on the left" ever again!*

He chuckles at his daydream.

Avenue of the Stars! Come on, Jim-Bo, be a big time CD! Avenue of the Staaaaaarrrrrrrsssss!!!

GPS: In 400 hundred feet, pick up Jim on the right.

He glares at his phone.

I hate you…Come on, Jim! Be the man! Give me my big break!

He pulls up and sees Jim, who's smiling big and waving small. He's a stout guy with a barrel chest, bald head, and a goatee. His "parade float wave" seems very much out of character. Also, Mark knows his dream scenario is not going to happen...*Never seen a casting director wear a suit and tie.*

Jim gets in the car. He has an easygoing, Southern accent.

JIM: Hello, Mark.
MARK: Hey, Jim. How are you doing this evening?
JIM: Well, I'm doing just fine, sir, just fine.
MARK: I apologize for not greeting you with more Southern hospitality, but this is all I've got.
JIM: (chuckling) Oh, that's okay. It's fine by me.

Mark swipes the app and sees they are heading to Father's Office.

MARK: You're off to get burgers tonight, I see.
JIM: Yep. I'm only in town for a few days—doing a little work for a law firm over here—and I asked around. There was another place that people suggested, but it's closed on Mondays, so Father's Office it is. You ever been there?
MARK: Yeah, a couple of times. I think you'll enjoy it.
JIM: I'm sure I will, sir.

Mark smiles each time he hears the word, "sir."

MARK: So, where's home for you, Jim?
JIM: Atlanta.
MARK: Born and raised?
JIM: Nope. Grew up in a small town a little further south, but I've been in Atlanta for about fifteen years now, and I've got to say: I like it so much better.
MARK: Oh yeah. Why is it so much better?

Jim squirms, starts to answer, pauses, then tries again.

JIM: Well, let's just say, there's a lot less racism in Atlanta than where I grew up.
MARK: Really?
JIM: Yes. And take it from a guy who doesn't care about any of that stuff—what race you are and all. I don't care who you are, what you look like, or what you believe in. I'll sit down with anyone. Have a meal, watch a movie, anything ... Trust me: it was really bad.

Mark glances in the rearview mirror; Jim's uneasiness has sparked his curiosity.

MARK: So, look, we don't have to go too deep into this if you don't want to, but I'm a guy from L.A. Yeah, I'm well aware of racism and seen racism, but Los Angeles is very different than even Atlanta, let alone where you grew up. I'm just curious—from your perspective—are things getting better or is it just recycling from generation to generation?

This time Jim is not hesitant.

JIM: It's recycling. Let me tell you something: Kids aren't born like that. They don't care about skin color or gender or anything else. They'll play together without thought. But—
MARK: —They are taught.
JIM: Yep. It's passed right down to them.

He takes a moment to gather his thoughts, then leans forward.

JIM: It's like this: Despite our differences, people just need to accept people.

MARK: "People just need to accept people." Pretty simple when you put it that way.

Jim nods, sits back, and then stares out the window. Mark decides to change the subject.

MARK: Have you enjoyed your visit to Los Angeles?
JIM: It's nice. I like it. But kind of a funny place. I was out for a walk, and where I'm from, if you see someone along the way, you say hello. Not here. People even make it a point to not look at you.
MARK: (chuckling) Yeah, you've got that right. L.A. is a lot tougher than most realize. Unfortunately, many people are only friendly when they think you can do something for them. Then everyone else puts up walls because they're worried about that very thing. It just feeds upon itself. Don't get me wrong: there are plenty of great people, but it can be pretty cutthroat. Truth is, having real friendships can be very difficult.

They stop at a red light. Mark reflects on his words and compares them to Jim's from moments earlier...*I suppose there's good people and bad people everywhere. They're just designed differently.*

For the rest of the trip the two simply talk about college football.

JIM: Love me my Daaawwwgs!
MARK: Nice.
JIM: Saturdays, everyone comes over, I get the smoker going, and we just eat and watch the Dawgs.
MARK: That sounds like a great day. What do you cook up?
JIM: Ribs, brisket, and pulled pork are my specialties.
MARK: Oooooo, man, that sounds good. I should come visit.
JIM: Come on down!

MARK: Ya know what—I might just have to do that someday. I bet you make a great host.
JIM: I certainly try.

They pull up to Father's Office.

MARK: Enjoy your burger, Jim. It was great talking with you, sir.
JIM: I will, and it was great talking to you too. You have yourself a good evening.

Jim hands over a five-dollar bill and heads out. Meanwhile, Mark shakes his head as he pulls away from the curb...*Man, if only everyone could be like my new dawg, Jim.*

**"Great Ride.
Great Conversation."**

★★★★★

"KNEE DEEP"

Early mornings on the weekend are Mark's favorite time to drive. Traffic is minimal (a Los Angeles miracle), there's plenty of people needing rides, and passengers are mellow. He also gets his fair share of laughs during these hours. He's listened to tales of one-night stands and drunken adventures, and many times he's heard the phrase "I know it's around here somewhere" while circling neighborhoods where the rider had left their car the night before. The stories are rarely dull and often lean toward hilarity.

So, as he gets in his car on a mid-August Saturday morning, he's hoping for an interesting ride or two. His first trip takes him downtown. His passenger, *Julie*, is nice but rather dull, and she prefers to listen to music than have a conversation. Fortunately, the app soon chimes, and Mark heads to his next pickup location just a few blocks away.

He pulls up to a modern tower that stands high above the old brick buildings that line the rest of the street. He double checks the app to make sure he's in the right spot, then patiently waits for *Melody*. After five minutes he calls.

MELODY: Hello?
MARK: Hi Melody, it's your Uber driver, just wanted to let you know that I'm here.

MELODY: Okay, thanks. My friends will be out in a moment.

Oh boy. Been there, done that.

Fortunately, on this day, he doesn't have to wait too long as two well-built men in their early twenties soon hobble out of the building. One is wearing a beanie—which is strange considering it's a warm, mid-summer's morning—while the other hurriedly puts on sunglasses as if he hasn't been outside in a month. What also catches Mark's eye is the large leg braces both men are wearing.

MARK: Damn, guys, Melody must be pretty wild. It looks like she worked you both over.

The two of them laugh, but *Beanie* has a quick retort.

BEANIE: No, we're underground fighters.

Mark looks in the rearview mirror. Neither man has any visible cuts or bruises, and the "underground fighter" story seems rather ridiculous.

MARK: Commmmmeeee on.
BEANIE: No, I'm playin'. We're football players.

A Los Angeles Rams logo is stitched on his cap, and Mark sees their destination is UC Irvine where the Rams are training.

MARK: You guys play for the Rams?
BEANIE: We're trying out. We're undrafted free agents.
MARK: Cool. What position do you play?
SUNGLASSES: I'm a wide receiver.
BEANIE: I'm a defensive back.

MARK: Nice. Where did you play your college ball?
BEANIE: Tennessee.
MARK: Ah, SEC (Southeastern Conference) country.
BEANIE AND SUNGLASSES: You know it!
MARK: I suppose I'll still let you stay in the car.

He winks; they laugh.

BEANIE: You a fan?
MARK: College I am. Not so much the NFL any longer, but it's cool that the Rams are back in L.A.

Sunglasses begins making a phone call, but Beanie stays engaged in the conversation.

BEANIE: Who's your college squad?
MARK: UCLA.
BEANIE: Okay, okay.
MARK: Yeah, it's been a tough little stretch, but I'm always cautiously optimistic heading into a season.
BEANIE: No doubt.

As the ride continues, Mark asks questions about playing at Tennessee, what Rams' Coach Jeff Fischer is like, and the differences between college and pro ball. Being the huge sports fan that he is, the conversation is a dream come true.

MARK: How's camp been going?
BEANIE: It was going pretty well, the coaches seemed to like me, then the injury happened.
MARK: Yeah, that looks serious. What happened?
BEANIE: Tore my ACL.
MARK: Oooooo! Damn, man, I'm sorry.

BEANIE: Thanks. Weird thing was: I wasn't even hit; I just planted and it went.
MARK: Damn.
BEANIE: We're both heading back to Tennessee for rehab.

Mark nods, but he also wonders if this could be it for them. He knows that making an NFL roster is next to impossible, but it's that much more difficult as an undrafted free agent...*And now a serious injury? Shoot, just losing one-tenth of a second in speed could be too much for them to overcome.*

However, he quickly pushes away his "Donny Downer" thoughts when a brighter realization comes to mind.

MARK: Wait, you guys are on this year's *Hard Knocks.*
BEANIE: Yup.
MARK: That's cool.

Hard Knocks, The HBO documentary series, which follows one NFL team through training camp, pre-season, and up to the regular season, is riveting. The athletes that fans only know from afar become humanized. Dreams are realized or fade away forever; the emotion on both sides of the coin is tantalizing to watch.

MARK: I saw the first episode. Are you in it at all?
BEANIE: Not the first one, but word is that I'm in a lot of last week's. They show my injury.
MARK: Oh...Um...You haven't seen it?
BEANIE: Nah. I don't want to.

Beanie's voice trails off and he looks solemnly out the window.

Dammit, why did you bring that up? You know he got hurt.

Nothing else is said for the rest of the trip.

A half hour later, they arrive at UC Irvine. The two gentlemen make their way out of the car in a slow and deliberate manner.

MARK: It was good talking to you both. I hope rehab goes well and you get your shot.
BEANIE: Thanks. And thanks for the ride. I appreciate you.

And there it is: Mark's favorite salutation of a departing passenger—"*I appreciate you.*" Every once in a while he hears that exact phrase, and while he'd much rather be making his living solely from acting work, each time he hears "I appreciate you," he's reminded that helpful acts—big and small—are still needed and valued. He hopes his sincere wishes have been equally cherished.

Later in the day he watches the latest episode of *Hard Knocks,* and sure enough, the coaches were falling in love with Beanie. He wasn't the most talented player on the field, but he showed a great work ethic, a willingness to learn, and was doing everything he could to make the team…And then the injury.

Damn. Such a cool dude too. Hope he makes it back.

The TV is turned off, Mark grabs his keys, and heads out for another session…*Just goes to show you: One's dreams can be realized or shattered in a fraction of time…On any given day…When you least expect it.*

"Good Guy"

★★★★★

"GUILTY OF IMPERSONATION"

AUGUST 18, 2016

Mark is standing in a courtroom. His mouth is dry. His thoughts are jumbled. His heart is thumping against his chest...Just as it has for the last four hours.

He timidly looks up. The judge averts his eyes. The opposing attorney smiles sympathetically, but it doesn't help...*Please say it already. Just say it already!*

1ST ASSISTANT DIRECTOR: That's a wrap on this location!

With a thud, Mark plops onto his chair. He scans the room; no one looks at him. He gulps while closing his eyes.

What the fuck just happened?...

Actors are an antsy bunch as is, but when May hits and the "Summer Slowdown" kicks in, they become unbearable. Agents and managers send out preemptive emails to remind their clients that auditions *will* slow down for the next few months. Actors prep their mind for the dip, but when it happens, they freak out. The statement

"Why am I not going out?!!" is uttered at least three times a day. It's as if they lose all capacity to read a calendar.

Mark, however, is feeling much calmer than usual. His successful first half of the year has helped him not sweat the dead period. But as money diminishes and being an Uber driver takes on a heavier load, his anxiety begins to return.

A week after the 4th of July he calls his agent, Mariko, to see if the town has gotten any busier.

MARK: Yo, Mariko, how goes it out there?
MARIKO: Yo, MB, it's still slow, but starting to pick up.
MARK: Okay. Just getting a little restless.
MARIKO: I know you are. Be patient; auditions will be coming soon.
MARK: Okay, thanks. Talk later.

The two first met twenty years earlier when Mariko was a commercial casting director and Mark enrolled in her auditioning class. Over time, they stayed in touch and finally teamed up when she shifted from CD to agent while he was looking for new representation. The first nine months together have been fruitful. Plus, Mark appreciates Mariko's straight-shooter style while still managing to be one of the nicest people in Hollywood (a rare mix).

Along with Mariko, he is also represented by a management company. Traditionally, a manager's role is to oversee their clients' careers: public relations, money matters, which projects to take and which to pass on. In the past, only very successful actors employed managers, but now even actors with limited resumes often use teams, primarily to help procure more auditions.

Mark has had his share of management teams over the years, but he's never been with a better group than the one he's with now. His audition opportunities skyrocketed the moment he signed with them at the end of 2015, and much of his recent success is due to their hustle and gumption.

Still—as with most relationships—there are concerns. First, while auditions have been coming in steadily, many of the roles don't fit his personality, age, or look. The fact that his managers can even get him "in the room" for these parts—despite the specs suggesting an entirely different type of actor—always astonishes him, but it can also feel like a giant waste of time.

However, he *also* knows every opportunity is a blessing. So instead of griping, he's taken on a much more positive attitude...*Anytime you get in front of a casting director it's a win.*

He's taken on the mantra "Book the room, not the job", knowing that if he has a good read, the casting director will take notice and somewhere down the road will bring him in for a role that's much more appropriate. Admittedly, that attitude doesn't always fly when he's sitting in bumper to bumper traffic on the 405 freeway while heading to a "pointless" audition...*Book the room, not the job. Book the room, not the job.*

But his biggest issue with his managers is their lack of personal attention. While they have an open-door policy to discuss one's career, he never hears from them. He understands they're busy, but after six TV bookings and a movie in five months, he's surprised he's not received a single call. Perhaps a "Congratulations on all your success, let's talk about how to take the next step" call or a "How was shooting the movie in Missouri? Was it a good experience?"

call. After all, they are his *managers*, the ones guiding his career. But his phone never rings.

Then one day it surprisingly does.

MARK: Hey, guys! What's up?
MANAGERS: Well, we're thinking you need some new headshots.
MARK: New headshots? Seems like the current ones are doing really well.
MANAGERS: Yes, the ones you have are fine, but we'd like you to get some different ones too.
MARK: Different ones?
MANAGERS: We want you to grow out a full beard and mustache, then take some shots wearing a leather jacket.

???

MARK: Are you sure you guys called the right "Mark?"
MANAGERS: (laughing) Yes, we're sure. We just think it would get you more auditions.
MARK: Guys, no offense, but I'm a near fifty-year-old, skinny, Jew. I don't think I'm ever going to play a badass.
MANAGERS: Well, we had another client do the same thing, and he started going out way more than he had been.
MARK: Ummmmmm, I suppose I could—
MANAGERS: Look, you don't have to do it if you don't want to.
MARK: It just seems odd. Maybe we could focus on bigger parts that I'm right for, like the one I played in that movie *School Spirits.* I should tell you about it.
MANAGERS: Yeah, come in one day, we'll talk about it, but in the meantime, give this some thought. And since you're a photographer, you can just take some pics of yourself, so it won't cost you anything.

MARK: Yeah...um...okay.

They hang up...*That was definitely not the conversation I've been waiting to have.*

He leans back, releases a sigh, and shakes his head. Suddenly, he feels like a tiny cog in their giant machine and questions whether they're trying to help him get to the next step in his career. Since managers and agents can have as many clients as they desire, if a bunch of tiny cogs are consistently getting work, the machine is doing quite well. But those tiny cogs?—They still need three jobs to pay their rent.

Still, in an attempt to appease them, he grows out his beard and takes some photos.

MANAGERS: Can you let it grow out for another month and try again?
MARK: Sorry, guys, it's itching like crazy; it's driving me nuts.
MANAGERS: Yeah, okay. No problem.

The conversation signifies the end of Mark's badass era.

By the time August rolls around, the town starts picking up. A few auditions come in, but the gigs don't go Mark's way. He's not overly concerned, however; he feels he's auditioning well and will book one soon enough.

After a few more go by the wayside, he's invited to read for the role of an attorney on *Grey's Anatomy*. He's auditioned at this casting office many times before. The CD's are always friendly and encouraging, especially one, who often greets actors with a big smile and a vote of confidence—"Today is going to be the one, I can feel it!"

Such a simple welcome may not seem like much, but it can sure help calm an actor's jumpy nerves.

As Mark waits, he bounces the lines in his head. Reading for medical and legal shows can be difficult because professional jargon is often injected into the script. Consequently, the dialogue doesn't always flow naturally. Even very seasoned actors have had their fair share of mishaps because of "procedural dialogue."

Fortunately, he hasn't noticed any verbal potholes in the scene; the few lines—and one relatively long speech—seem to be catered to him.

He's all ready to go when the encouraging CD walks by.

CD: Hey, Mr. Bloom, good to see you. I think today is going to be the day.

Mark smiles and soon makes his way into the auditioning room. There, he senses the casting director might just be right: his read is solid. He leaves the office with some extra spring in his step, believing the role could be his.

Saturday and Sunday are filled with driving and hanging out with friends. The potential of some great news the following week makes the weekend more palatable than usual. Oddly, Mark is not a fan of weekends. With no money to go out nor the chance of a new audition until the following week, weekends can be grueling. Consequently—and unlike most everyone else on the planet—his least favorite day of the week is Friday while his favorite is Monday. His acting friends get it, his *normal* friends don't.

Monday comes, and the wait is worth it: He's "pinned" for *Grey's Anatomy*, meaning the director and producers have narrowed down their choices to just a few actors. The news is exciting. He knows if he books the role the year's momentum will keep surging forward, he'll earn some needed money, and it could lead to some great exposure.

Over the next few days, he jumps every time the phone rings, but it takes an entire week until he hears anything further. Finally, Mariko receives an email from casting, informing her that he's "the choice" and they're just getting "network approval."

Later in the day, she calls.

MARK: Hey there, do you have good news for me?
MARIKO: I do. You're booked on *Grey's*. The wardrobe fitting is on Wednesday and you shoot on Thursday.
MARK: Nice!
MARIKO: Congratulations, MB. Call me after the shoot and let me know how it went.
MARK: I will. And thanks as always.

When he arrives at the wardrobe fitting, the lead stylist has a surprise for him.

STYLIST: Here are your new sides (script).
MARK: Wait; I'm not doing the scene I did for casting?
STYLIST: Nope.

It's not uncommon for popular shows to use mock sides for auditions so that storylines don't leak to the public, but the switch has startled him. Quickly he grabs the new script…*Uh-oh*…No longer is it an intimate scene taking place in a judge's chamber; instead, it will be taking place in a courtroom setting.

While the setting is different, he knows the location change is no big deal as long as the dialogue is the same—it's not. The content is similar, but the speech is no longer streamlined. Immediately, his stomach churns.

Will you relax?! You've been on over twenty shows without barely a hiccup. You're fine. You're a professional. Do not let this trip you up.

The next morning he arrives on set. He's worked on the dialogue all night, and despite the awkwardness of the speech, he believes he's got it down.

After getting his hair and makeup done, he meets his fellow scene partners: one is playing the "judge", one is playing the "defense attorney." As they sit in the holding area, the judge suggests they do a run through. Everything starts out fine, but when Mark gets to his speech, the words don't come out; he has to look to the sides for help.

MARK: Hey, can we do that again?
FELLOW ACTORS: Yeah, of course.

The second run is even worse. He feels himself beginning to tighten…*Do not trip yourself up.*

They try a third time. Again, he has to reference the sides to get the words out.

Just then, the first assistant director enters the room.

FIRST AD: Follow me, guys. We're going to do a rehearsal with the director.

They all walk out to the scene's location: a large space that has been converted into a courtroom. 60 to 70 background actors are filling the pews while a few regular *Grey's* cast members are milling around.

DIRECTOR: Okay, let's give it a try.

They begin, but like a Pavlovian dog, when Mark gets to the speech, the words become foreign once more. He awkwardly babbles out the dialogue while looking at the sides. No one says a thing. Beads of sweat begin traversing down his back.

DIRECTOR: All right, let's shoot this.

Everyone takes their places. The woman playing the defense attorney leans over.

DEFENSE ATTORNEY: You got this.

But Mark is so deep in his head he barely hears her. He checks his sides one last time, tucks them into his suit jacket, takes a deep breath, and hopes for the best.

"The best" does not happen…First take—stumble. Second take—fumble…3rd take—trip. He can't get the dialogue out to save himself. He begins saying words that don't even make sense. With each mistake he withdraws further into his head… *What the fuck! Just say the lines!…*He can feel everyone around him becoming increasingly uncomfortable...*Shit!*...He checks the sides between each take. He admonishes himself. He encourages himself. He tries a million different ways to shake out of the funk he's gotten himself into...Nothing helps. At one point there's a close-up on one of the other actors. Mark isn't even shown and can literally read the words from the script—he still doesn't get it right...*Are you friggin' kidding me!*...It's a complete and total disaster. Yet no one—not even the director—says a word to him. He's on his own—sink or swim. What he truly wants is for someone to come over and push him in the chest, believing the blow would stir the "fight" in him and counter the flight instincts that have completely taken over his being... But no one approaches.

The cameras are moved. The director pops his head in the room.

DIRECTOR: Hey, Mark, this one's on you—your close-up.

Oh shit. All right, come on, come on. You can do this...YOU CAN DO THIS!

DIRECTOR: Annnnndddd...ACTION!

Miraculously, for the first time all day, the words come together. The two takes aren't perfect but they're close. He feels some sense of redemption.

As the cameras move again, the actors are given a brief break.

DEFENSE ATTORNEY: Hey, you nailed your close-ups. I knew you would.
MARK: Thanks. I really apologize to you both. This is so embarrassing; I feel like a complete amateur. I don't even know what's happening.

JUDGE: You're doing fine. It happens to everyone.
DEFENSE ATTORNEY: Yeah, don't worry. They'll be able to cut it together and you'll never know the difference.

Deep down he knows she's right: the editors will take bits and pieces of each take and put them together to make a seamless cut…But he still finds the whole day to be horrifying.

After the break, there're more angles to shoot. Unfortunately, he falls right back to his stumbling ways.

Finally, four hours after they first began, the first AD bellows out the words Mark's been longing to hear.

FIRST AD: That's a wrap on this location!

…It takes five minutes for his heart rate to return to normal. He sits like a statue and watches the courtroom steadily empty. Eventually, he finds the strength to stand. He searches out the director.

MARK: I am so sorry.
DIRECTOR: No problem. You were great.
MARK: Um…yeah…okay, thanks.

He knows the director is simply being kind. Truth is, if a stand-in actor had been on set, he would have been fired within minutes.

He shakes the director's hand and trudges his way to his trailer.

What should I do now? What happened? Should I still act? Years of working hard on this craft and this happens?! Word will get back to casting about this. They'll never invite me back to audition for one of their shows.

He enters his trailer and takes a seat. His head falls into his hands. Thoughts churn. He's sick to his stomach. Finally, after ten motionless minutes, he looks up and checks his phone. There, he finds one missed call and an awaiting voicemail. He looks closer—reads the name on the screen…*Oh God, no.*

The call is from his managers…His managers, who never…*ever*… call.

He paces back and forth for minutes. Eventually, he gets the nerve to play the message.

MANAGERS: Hey, Mark. The moment you get this, call us back.

Holy fuck-Holy fuck-Holy fuck.

He feels like a three-year-old who's about to be admonished by his parents for spreading peanut butter over their freshly painted living room walls…*They may drop me from their roster. Shit!… Shit!-Shit!-Shit!*

Knowing there's nothing else he can do, he calls.

MARK: Hey, it's Mark.
MANAGER: Hey…Um, are you all right?
MARK: Uh, no. I just had the worst day on set.
MANAGER: What happened?

MARK: I couldn't get my lines out for four hours straight. I assumed someone called you and that's what your message was about.
MANAGER: No. We just wanted to see if you would take pictures of the party we're throwing. We're not paying anything, but it could give your photography business some exposure.

Whew!

MARK: Oh. Um…okay. Um…Let me think about it. My mind is not really in a good place right now.
MANAGER: Don't worry about that. It happens to everyone.
MARK: Yeah…um…Let me call you tomorrow. I've got a lotta things to think about.
MANAGER: Okay.

Twenty minutes later, he climbs into his car and calls his friend and acting buddy, Kristen, to vent about the day's events.

KRISTEN: ...Oh, wow. I'm so sorry that happened.
MARK: Yeah, me too. It was a nightmare.
KRISTEN: I'm sure it wasn't as bad as you think.
MARK: Kristen, it was even worse than I described. They should have put me on trial for impersonating an actor.
KRISTEN: Well, try to find something that will take your mind off of things. If you need me, just give me a call.
MARK: Thanks.

As they hang up, he looks right and sees his distraction: The Uber sticker on the front windshield beckons him…*Might as well. Going by your performance today this may be your only source of income moving forward…*He pulls out his phone, prompts the app, and heads out—hoping with all hope, that the day's events will soon wash from his consciousness.

*Six weeks later, he gets home from a night of driving, logs onto Facebook, and finds a message from a friend—"Hey, I just saw a promo for the latest episode of Grey's Anatomy: You're all over it! Congratulations!"

He finds the advertisement online and sees that the nightmare scene comprises the entire promo...*Are you kidding me?!*

While he knew the editors could cut the footage together and make the scene look respectable, he finds the use of his "work" for the promo to be surreal. He sits back and can't help but laugh at the absurdity of it all.

Ah yes: The magic that is Hollywood.

"JUMP IN THE POOL! THE WATER'S FINE!"

It's a Wednesday evening. Mark begins a pool by picking up *Rod* in the business section of Beverly Hills.

MARK: Hey, Rod, how ya doin'?
ROD: Good. Just getting off work and looking forward to getting home.
MARK: All right, let's get you there.

The app chimes as they head out of Beverly Hills, signifying another rider has been added. Mark quickly takes a right turn.

ROD: No, man, you should have gone straight there.
MARK: Oh, sorry, we need to pick up another passenger.
ROD: Wait! Did I order a pool?!
MARK: Yep.
ROD: Oh no, I need to get out. Pools take way too long.

Mark understands, but he doesn't want Rod to have to pay for an extra trip if he doesn't have to.

MARK: What if we do this?—I'll turn off the app, so it won't accept any more requests. Then, once we pick up this second passenger, we can see who's getting dropped off first. If it's them, I can let you out; if it's you, you'll get home in the same amount of time as if you had ordered an Uber X. How's that sound?

ROD: Cool. Thanks, man. I appreciate it.

I appreciate YOU. I appreciate YOU. You were so close, Rod.

A final right turn leads them to the pick-up spot. Waiting are two very attractive women. They get in. Mark checks the app.

MARK: Hey, my man, you're not the first drop-off. What do you want to do?

Rod looks at his fellow passengers.

ROD: Ya know, I think I'm cool. I'll just ride it out.

Yeah, that's what I thought you'd say.

ROD: So, ladies, what are you getting into this evening?...

"Thanks, Mark! Best Uber Ride Ever!"

★★★★★

"IT'S THURSDAY NIGHT LIVE!!!"

It's a Thursday night in Hollywood. Mark is in the middle of a pool.

A couple sits quietly in the backseat when a notification chimes in on the app; another rider, *Don,* will be joining them. They head west on Sunset Boulevard and follow the directions of the GPS. When they arrive, there's no sign of Don. Mark waits for another thirty seconds but is sensing that the couple is becoming restless. He decides to call.

DON: Hello?
MARK: Hi Don, it's your Uber driver. I'm just trying to find you.
DON: I'm in front of the Director's Guild.

Mark mutters towards the app.

DON: What was that?
MARK: Um, nothing. I'll be right there.

He heads out. Unfortunately, he's gotten his Hollywood landmarks confused and ends up in front of the wrong building.

MARK: Shit, that's not the Director's Guild.
COUPLE: Are you going to go back and get him?
MARK: Yeah. Sorry, guys.

They say nothing.

Mark grumbles, drives back to the original spot, and there's Don, waiting patiently on the sidewalk.

MARK: Hi. Sorry about that. I got a little confused.
DON: Oh, don't worry. I've made mistakes too. (he looks to the backseat) Hello.
COUPLE: Hi.

They begin heading towards Koreatown to drop off the couple.

MARK: So, what was going on at the DGA?
DON: There was a pre-*Emmys* show. Some special awards, that sort of thing.
MARK: Were you there supporting someone?
DON: No…Um, actually, I was being honored.

Mark sits taller.

MARK: You were being honored? Pardon my rudeness, but who are you?
DON: My name is Don Roy King, and for the last ten years I've had the pleasure of being the director of *Saturday Night Live.*
MARK: What?! That's so cool. Are you the only director? I've always assumed there's a variety.
DON: Nope. Just me. I took over in 2006.
MARK: This is awesome! I've got the director of *Saturday Night Live* in my car!
DON: It's not that big of a deal.

Mark and the couple disagree.

MARK: What's it like being the director of *SNL?*
DON: Fantastic. Best job I ever had. The people are generous, extremely talented, and inspiring. Every day there is a blessing.

As the ride continues, Don has found himself surrounded by a very captive audience.

DON: Ya know, I earned my first award in the 70s for the *Mike Douglas Show* and for the next two years…

He pauses and looks over.

DON: …I became an asshole.
MARK: What?! You? No! You seem like the nicest guy.
DON: Well, I wasn't then. I got a big head, thought it was all about me. I was an ass.
MARK: Wow.
DON: And then I realized it wasn't about me; it was about the team. I've appreciated my job and the people I work with ever since.

He continues reciting stories and lists some of his favorite *SNL* cast members and skits. As they stop at a red light, he finishes describing one of his favorite sketches.

MARK: Oh, I haven't seen that one. I don't watch very often.

!!!!!!!

A hush comes over the car… *Why? Why?? WHY?!? would you say that?!*

Don looks over at his increasingly red-cheeked driver.

MARK: I just meant that I'm usually asleep.

In succession: Don laughs, the couple laughs, Mark laughs.

As they make their way through the streets of L.A., Don discusses the restaurant that the couple are heading to, then he switches his attention.

DON: So, Mark, what do you do when you're not an Uber driver?
MARK: Well, I'm actually an actor.
COUPLE: And you told the director of *Saturday Night Live* that you don't watch the show?!

Everyone laughs.

MARK: I didn't say I was a *smart* actor.
DON: Ha! So, how's it going?
MARK: Well…

He wants to be humble, but he's having the best year of his career, <u>and</u> the director of *Saturday Night Live* is in his car…*This is not the time to be shy, pal.*

MARK: …Things have been good. I've been on seven shows so far this year and had a nice part in a movie.
DON: Really? What shows?
MARK: *Black-ish, Silicon Valley*…uh, *Grey's Anatomy.*

With a shade of paranoia, he looks around to see if any of his passengers have become privy to the *Grey's* debacle. To his relief, no one bats an eye.

DON: Wow! That's great.

MARK: It's all right. Always trying to take that next step.
DON: I understand. But it sounds like you're doing well.
MARK: I suppose. Although here I am: still driving for Uber on a Thursday night, soooo…
DON: Yeah, I get it.
MARK: But hey, I've got the director of *SNL* in my car, so there's that.

The couple applauds in agreement.

Minutes later, they arrive at the couple's destination. Don wishes them a good night then the trip continues towards downtown.

DON: Do you do improv?
MARK: I've tried it a little over the years. The last class I took was "long-form" improv; wasn't my thing. Maybe "short-form" would be a better fit.
DON: It certainly's not for everyone.
MARK: Hey, speaking of improv, have you seen the movie *Don't Think Twice?*
DON: The one about the Improv group?
MARK: Yeah. Part of it deals with a faux *Saturday Night Live.* I was just curious what you might have thought since you're in that world.
DON: Well, my wife and I went to see it, but it was sold out. Did you see it?
MARK: I did.
DON: What did you think?

Mark hesitates.

MARK: You sure you want my review?
DON: Yeah, I'll see it no matter what you say, so let it rip.

MARK: Okay…I thought it was terrible.
DON: Really?!
MARK: Yep. I was surprised, too, because I like all the actors in it. If I hadn't been with my friend, Kim, I would have walked out. After we left, I asked her what she thought; she had the same opinion. Everyone else in the theater seemed to enjoy it, and it's got a '98' on *Rotten Tomatoes,* so I don't know what to tell you. Kim and I must have been in a parallel universe and saw something completely different than everyone else. Subjective material, right? I hope what I said didn't ruin it for you.
DON: It's okay. I'll still go see it.

They pull up to Don's hotel.

DON: Well, Mark, it was great meeting you.
MARK: Great meeting you too, sir.
DON: Good luck with everything.
MARK: Thank you.

Don begins to exit, but suddenly Mark has an idea.

MARK: Hey, let me give you my card.

Don turns and his smile drops. Mark immediately recognizes the expression.

MARK: Oh, no-no-no! I'm not giving it to you for acting—I'd never be so presumptuous. No, take the card—my number is on there—and after you see the movie, call me, and tell me know what you thought.

The smile returns to Don's face. He grips the card a little tighter.

DON: I'll do that. Goodnight.
MARK: Goodnight.

*Mark felt like there was a 50/50 shot he'd get a call, but he never did hear from Don. Yet despite not getting a chance to play *Siskel and Ebert* with the director of *SNL*, he still believes Don Roy King is about as pleasant a person as he's ever met.

"Mark, thanks for the ride and good conversation. Stay blunt."

★★★★★

"DO AS I WEAR, NOT AS I DO"

Mark is sitting in his car on a lovely Wednesday afternoon in Pasadena. He checks his phone to see if any audition notifications have come in. Nothing. While releasing a sigh, he looks left and sees his passenger, *Marnie,* making her way to the car. She's wearing baggy shorts and an even baggier t-shirt with the words "DON'T TAKE CANDY FROM STRANGERS" printed in huge "Frankie Says Relax" font across the front.

The edges of Mark's lips rise ever so slightly.

As Marnie gets settled in the backseat, he can't resist: He reaches forward and grabs a container of Ice Breaker mints, holds it up, and shakes it enticingly.

MARK: Mint?
MARNIE: Oh yes, thanks.

She takes a couple of the tasty treats, returns the container, and, unaware of the irony, sits back to enjoy her fifteen-minute ride through the well-manicured streets of Pasadena.

MARNIE: Thanks so much.
MARK: No problem. The pleasure is truly all mine.

The tiny smile on Mark's face grows to a sly grin, and a joyful chuckle bounds around his soul for the next half-hour.

"Very polite and gracious."

★★★★★

"THE NEWLY-DEADS?"

It's a beautiful Sunday morning. Mark pulls up to an apartment building in Los Feliz to pick up *Scott*, who has ordered a pool. As he waits, a notification comes through the app—*Tiffany* will be joining them.

Scott exits his building and approaches the car. His hair is a mess, his head is down, a small backpack lays in his hands. He begins to get in the backseat, thinks better of it, and makes his way to the passenger seat instead.

MARK: Mornin', Scott. Just want to let you know we have another rider to pick up.
SCOTT: Yeah, Tiffany...I got the notice on my phone. *BING!*

Mark grins at the app imitation.

MARK: So, how's your weekend going?

Scott keeps his head down and fidgets with his backpack.

SCOTT: Ah, I don't know...Tough day.

Despite his disheveled look and "tough day" proclamation, there also seems to be some levity in his tone. However, Mark isn't sure how to interpret the mirth, along with the random fidgets, changing of seats, and sound effects.

MARK: Well, what's going on?
SCOTT: Having some marital problems.

His head lifts, and for the first time, Mark sees his eyes—they are dead *and* alive.

He begins to explain his predicament.

SCOTT: My wife wants me to get a tattoo of her name.
MARK: Ohhhh.
SCOTT: Yeah man, I don't know if I want to do it…(sighing) I guess I could get it removed someday if things don't work out.

Again, there's a dash of humor behind his words but with serious undertones. He's like a Rubik's Cube with seven sides—impossible to figure out.

MARK: Soooo, uh…How long have you guys been married?
SCOTT: A month.
MARK: Oh boy.
SCOTT: Yeah, I don't know what to think. This isn't good.
MARK: It'll be all right.
SCOTT: Yeah, maybe…Oh, and hey, can we not talk about this when we pick up Tiffany. Somehow she'll let my wife know. Women seem to be able to signal one other even if they're not friends.
MARK: (laughing) Right?! It's like they're connected by a radar or something. Beep, bop, boop, bop.

Scott looks over. He's not as impressed with Mark's sound effects as Mark was with his.

MARK: Sorry, I tried.

They pull up to Tiffany.

MARK: Good morning.
TIFFANY: Good morning.

She buckles up and immediately puts on headphones. The guys take note, look to one another, and nod—they can continue their conversation.

MARK: So, when are you getting the tattoo?
SCOTT: Now.
MARK: Now!?!
SCOTT: Now. I'm going to a friend's and then he's taking me.

He doesn't want to laugh too hard, but Mark's getting a big kick out of the situation. Scott, however, is getting more panicky by the second but in a Scott sort of way—even keeled panic.

MARK: And your wife didn't want to come along?
SCOTT: No.
MARK: Oh, that's not good. Why didn't she want to come along?
SCOTT: I don't know. She should have come along, right?
MARK: Absolutely. You can't mess this up, man. What if you come home and she says—
SCOTT: —That's not what I wanted!
MARK: Exactly.

Scott presses his head firmly against the back of his seat. His eyes roll upwards.

SCOTT: This isn't good.
MARK: No, it's not: she should have come along. And, hey, don't even think about spelling her name wrong.
SCOTT: I know, right?! I mean, I've checked it a million times. Her name's *Sherry,* but even though I know how it's spelled, I start freaking out. Is it Sherry with a "y?" With an "i?" With an "ie?"
MARK: And is it one "R" or two?
SCOTT: Oh shit, I didn't even think about that!!!

The two lose it and explode with laughter. It takes a moment, but Mark regroups and checks on Tiffany. She doesn't appear to be paying any attention to the conversation up front. Soon they reach her destination.

TIFFANY: Thanks. Have a great day.
MARK AND SCOTT: You too.

The door is shut.

MARK: I don't think Tiffany poses a threat.
SCOTT: Yeah, I think you're right.

As the ride continues, the guys quiet down—Scott is deep in thought; Mark is imagining all that might go wrong. Eventually he breaks the ice.

MARK: Ya know, I really think your wife should have come along.
SCOTT: Yep, she definitely should have come along.
MARK: And why again didn't she come along?
SCOTT: I still have no clue.

They arrive. Mark puts out his hand; Scott gives it a firm shake.

MARK: Good luck, brother.
SCOTT: Thanks, brother.

The male bonding ritual has concluded.

Scott begins exiting the car. He appears confident, yet gloriously disheveled…*He's a living-breathing oxymoron.*

As he watches his new bud walk away, Mark decides it would be wise to dole out one last reminder. He rolls down the window.

MARK: Hey, Scott!
SCOTT: Yeah?
MARK: Do me one favor.
SCOTT: What's that?
MARK: Make sure you spell her name correctly.

Scott takes in the advice and nods.

In return, Mark gives a thumbs up and pulls away.

She definitely should have come along.

"Mark was a hero of a driver. I wish him nothing but the best."

"THE WORLD KEEPS SPINNING"

Mark wakes up on a Wednesday morning with red, weary eyes. He immediately shuts them, hoping that by doing so, the thoughts running through his head will stop—they don't.

His usual wake-up routine consists of lying in bed, doing a little stretch routine, and browsing various social media apps—Facebook, then Instagram, and finally, his favorite, Twitter. But not today. Instead, he lies still, engulfed in the comfort and safety that a warm bed can elicit. He stares at the ceiling fan above him going around and around. Frankly, he's surprised that anything is still spinning properly, including Mother Earth.

A text comes in, but instead of checking it, he tosses the phone to the far end of the bed. Minutes pass without him moving a muscle. He thinks about his dad—a man of quality and substance. Mark would like to give him a call, talk to him for a little while, get some advice on how to move forward. But he can't.

Not sure you would have survived this anyway, Pop. I miss you... Sorry, I probably should have done more.

He shakes his head to clear out the cobwebs, knowing full well *his* life has to move on. He swings his feet around to the floor and slouches over his thighs. He has no appetite, doesn't want to browse the Internet, and certainly doesn't want to watch TV.

Screw it, might as well go make some money.

He staggers out of the apartment and into his car. As the engine warms, he adjusts the rearview mirror and catches his reflection. He can't bear to look at himself. He snaps his head away.

You should have done more.

Soon a request comes in.

As he pulls up, he recognizes the expression on the passenger's face—it's the same as the one he saw in the rearview mirror: listless, numb, dumbfounded. The passenger gets in the car, says nothing. Mark decides to break the ice, but quietly.

MARK: How are you doing?

The passenger makes no eye contact.

PASSENGER: I'm okay.

For a moment neither say a word, but Mark feels the need to say something—*anything*—even if it's a lie.

MARK: Everything will be all right.
PASSENGER: I hope so.
MARK: Yeah…I hope so too.

The tone of the day has been set: He drives for five hours, and literally everyone who enters his car is in the same funk. Feelings of despair and confusion live in all of them. It's as if every molecule of oxygen has been siphoned from the atmosphere and no one can breathe. Conversation is non-existent, smiles are forged by empathy—not confidence—everyone is sharing the same emotions without having to say a word. A few passengers are so despondent Mark wants to pull over and give them a hug. Instead, he simply drives them to their destination. Life has to move on. It does.

It's Wednesday, November 9, 2016, and just a few hours earlier, Donald J. Trump became the 45th President of the United States of America.

* * *

Later in the day, he heads out for another session. His first pick up is an elderly man. He, too, is despondent.

ELDERLY MAN: I spoke with my brother earlier today; he lives in Michigan. He said people in his neighborhood were hanging up Confederate Flags outside their homes.
MARK: No!
ELDERLY MAN: Yes.
MARK: Confederate Flags in *Michigan?*
ELDERLY MAN: Yes.
MARK: Wow.

He shakes his head and wonders what direction the country might soon travel under a Trump Presidency.

ELDERLY MAN: His supporters have been emboldened.
MARK: Yes, they have, and it's just the beginning.

The elderly man nods—nothing else needs to be said. They focus on their own thoughts until they reach the destination.

ELDERLY MAN: Good luck, young man.
MARK: Thank you, sir. You too.

The day has taken its toll. Mark turns off the app and drives home.

When he enters the front door, he heads straight for his bedroom and plops onto his bed where the day began. Again, he stares at the ceiling fan going around and around.

He's back home, but "home" no longer feels the same.

"God Bless"

★★★★★

"TURN AND FACE THE STRANGE... CH-CH-CH-CHANGES"

SUNDAY, NOVEMBER 13, 2016

It's a beautiful November day, and as Mark feels the sun hit the back of his neck, he spreads open a towel, kicks off his flip-flops, and enjoys the warm sand making its way between his toes.

He knows he's very fortunate to be living in Los Angeles. For all the complaints about L.A.: traffic, ego-centric people, more traffic, occasional smog (it's not nearly as bad as when he was a kid), and even *more* traffic, there's also an abundance of positives that his hometown brings to the table. There are great restaurants and nightlife, culture and a diverse population. You can visit the mountains or desert or forest or—today's choice—the beach, all within a couple of hours. Plus, the weather is tough to beat...*I'm having to put on sunblock in mid-November. This is pretty damn nice.*

On this day, he's met up with his very good friend, Kim, and her pal, Jen. He first met Kim on a commercial job when each was working as a production assistant. Over time, they've become very close friends (they call each other "budz") and have collaborated on many creative projects together. While Kim still works in the commercial world (as does Jen), she is also a fabulous writer and director, and the two constantly encourage one another to keep pursuing their creative dreams.

While the beach has become one of their favorite hang-out spots, on this day, they're finding it difficult to ignore the elephant in the sand.

KIM: I still can't believe Trump won.
JEN: Yeah, you, me, and half the country.
MARK: I'm afraid we're about to see some major changes—and not positive ones.
KIM AND JEN: No doubt.

The three vent their concerns, but soon decide they're not going to let politics ruin the day. And as Mark sits on his towel and looks out at the waves pleasantly breaking in the distance, he can't help but smile…*I'm on the beach, with great friends, on a sun-soaked November day. Things could be a lot worse*…It also doesn't hurt that the previous 48 hours have been very good to him…

Mark is clutching a script as he stands alone on a quiet sound stage. Behind him sit a long row of bleachers that in four days will be filled with a studio audience.

It's been three months since the *Grey's Anatomy* implosion. Since then, the acting world has not been kind to him. Auditions have been slow to come by, he and his managers are not seeing eye to eye, and he feels the momentum accrued at the beginning of the year has all but vanished. The downward trend has led to many stress-induced headaches and even more sleepless nights. But not on this day. On this day, his worries have subsided. On *this* day, he's happy.

After scanning the set, he looks down at the script. "*Dr. Ken*" is printed on the cover. It's Day One of rehearsals for the sitcom's Christmas episode, and while Mark hasn't done anything besides stand around so far, he's still having a blast.

This is pretty damn cool.

The experience is also being enhanced because it's the first time he'll be working on a "multi-cam" comedy, and he knows he's breaking through a tough Hollywood barrier. Reason being: Many casting directors are hesitant to hire an actor for a multi-cam until they have performed in front of a studio audience. It's the epitome of a Catch 22: "You can't audition for a multi-cam until you've worked on a multi-cam." However, a week earlier, he was surprisingly granted an audition, capitalized on it, and now will be able to put a multi-cam credit on his resume.

He begins flipping through the script when a voice lifts him from the pages.

VOICE: Mark, right?

He looks up to see the star of show, Ken Jeong, approaching with his hand extended.

MARK: Oh, hi.
KEN: How's it going? I saw your audition. You were really great. Very funny stuff.
MARK: Oh, thank you. Thanks for having me on the show.
KEN: It's our pleasure. Sorry that some of your comedic bits got cut.

MARK: No problem. Happy to play the straight man too.
KEN: Cool…Is everything good? Everyone treating you well?
MARK: Absolutely. Everyone's been great.
KEN: Good. Well, I just wanted to say hi. I'll see you a little later. And again, welcome.
MARK: Thank you.

With his mouth slightly agape, Mark watches Ken walk away.

Holy crap, Ken Jeong just said you were funny.

He scans his surroundings once more… *You're doing it, kid. You're doing it.*

…As he sits on the beach, enjoying the day with Kim and Jen, he can't help but think about how great it was to be welcomed to the show in such a kind manner. He decides it's the second best welcoming he's had, only topped a few years earlier when he worked on *Castle.*

On that occasion, upon entering his dressing room, he was greeted by a handwritten note from the show's star, Nathan Fillion. The message welcomed him to set and stated that if he needed anything to let Nathan know. The note concluded with the suggestion, "Let's have some fun." While an assistant most likely wrote the letter, the idea had obviously come from Mr. Fillion, and Mark found the gesture to be very encouraging. For "day players" it's always nice to feel part of the team. Television shows move so quickly that actors with small roles frequently get shuffled in-and-out before they can even enjoy the experience, and then it's back to the grind.

That day, Mark made a promise—"If I'm ever fortunate enough to be a series regular, I will follow the example of Mr. Fillion." It's as classy a move as he's ever seen in Hollywood.

The recollection leaves a satisfied grin on his face.

JEN: So, when do you shoot *Dr. Ken?*
MARK: Tuesday. The last day of rehearsal is tomorrow.
JEN: Very cool. Well, I probably shouldn't tell you this, but I may have more good news for you.
MARK: What's that?
JEN: I'm working on a Geico commercial that you auditioned for.
MARK: Actually, I had two Geico auditions recently. One was set at a restaurant with Julius Caesar standing on top of a Caesar's salad.
JEN: Yep, that's the one.
KIM: You're playing Julius Caesar?!!
MARK: No. I'd just be the dad of the family who's looking up at him.
KIM: Oh.
MARK: Hey, as long as I'm a principal it's no problem. I'll even play the salad if they want me to.
KIM: True that.

And it *is* true. Despite commercials not running as well as they used to, they can still help pay many bills and are far more lucrative than bit-parts on TV shows. Mark even once heard of a guy who made $400,000 on a single spot. Those days are long gone, but Geico commercials run well; booking one would be very helpful.

MARK: So, is that it?
JEN: No, the director loved you. You'll be getting a callback.
MARK: Nice. Did you tell him you knew me?
JEN: Yep. I was like, "Oh, that's a friend of mine." He really liked you. He was talking you up to the ad agency.

KIM: Niiiiiiiicccccceeee!
MARK: Well, I tell you what: If I book the spot, I'm taking us all out one day.
VOICE: Can I come too?

They all look up to see Kim's boyfriend, Anthony.

MARK: Absolutely! We're all going out! And it's on me!

The next day, he's back on the set of *Dr. Ken* for rehearsal Day 2. During a break, he checks his phone and sees a message from his managers: he's got a callback for Geico the following day.

No, no, no.

He quickly calls the office.

MANAGER: Did you get the callback notice?
MARK: Yeah, but I can't make it. I've got the *Dr. Ken* shoot tomorrow; I'll be here all day.
MANAGER: Well, I'll ask them if they can see you another time, or maybe they can just look at the original footage.
MARK: Okay, thanks.

His head drops…*There's no way they're going to see me on another day. Dammit!*

For the next couple of minutes, a series of obscenity laced thoughts circle his mind…*Shit! A commercial booking would guarantee next year's health benefits, not to mention all the upfront money. Son of a bi—…Oh, wait! Oh, wait-wait-wait.*

He quickly pulls out his phone, checks the details of the audition, and happily finds what he was hoping for: The callback is for the *other* Geico spot.

Thank you, thank you, thank you.

He dances in place, catching the eye of some of the *Dr. Ken* cast.

MARK: Sorry. Just some good news.

The following day he finally gets his chance to perform on a multi-cam comedy. It's a long afternoon and evening, but he finds the whole process—especially performing in front of a live audience—to be quite a rush.

At the end of the taping, each cast member comes out and takes a bow. The entire experience has been exhilarating, and as Mark lifts his head to see the applauding audience, he can't help but be proud of the new feather in his cap.

His positive momentum continues two days later when he officially gets a callback for the Geico spot that Jen is working on.

Unfortunately, the audition doesn't go as planned. The director pays no attention to him; instead, he focuses solely on the woman playing the wife.

He leaves the room not knowing what to think. . .*Did he already like me and not have to watch what I did?. . . Was someone else already cast?. . . Why didn't he give me any direction?!*

Rarely is there any feedback after auditions—aside from booking or not booking the role—and that's when the mental torture begins.

Actors have been known to ruminate over an audition for days if not weeks, all in an attempt to figure out what went wrong. Frequently it has nothing to do with their performance. However, trying to get an unemployed actor to halt the mental gymnastics routine going on in their head is near impossible.

Fortunately, on this occasion, Mark doesn't have to wait too long to find out his fate: An hour after leaving casting, he gets notified that he's been put on "avail" (the equivalent to being pinned in the commercial world). And while the job isn't officially his, his instincts are telling him he's got the role…*I can feel it.*

The next day, his prediction holds true, and the following week he's shooting a national commercial.

Between Geico and *Dr. Ken*, it's a fantastic finish to what has been (by far) his most successful acting year to date. But he wants more.

After much debate, he decides to not re-up his contract with his managers. While their hard work helped foster many auditions and eventual jobs, he feels there's something amiss. It's a big risk, but he senses there's something better out there for him.

Let's roll the dice. 2017, here I come!

*8 months later, on a beautiful Saturday morning, he drops off a passenger in Santa Monica, turns off the app, and calls Kim.

KIM: Hey, budz! What's up?
MARK: I'm in your area, and I'm gonna go grab some breakfast. Thought if you and Anthony hadn't eaten, you'd like to join me.

KIM: For sure. Jen is over, and we were just about to go out and get something. We'll see you soon.

A half hour later, the four end up at a trendy Santa Monica diner. Morning cocktails are downed, delicious food is devoured, and laughter bounces easily around the table. Halfway through the meal, Mark excuses himself and heads to the restroom. On the way, he sees the waitress and hands her his credit card.

MARK: When we're done, just charge it to my card, please.

He looks back at his friends, who are laughing and enjoying their meal…*It's no Nathan Fillion gesture, but for now it's the best I can do…And that's okay too.*

- 2017 -

"YO-GUH"

Mark is parked on a North Hollywood side street waiting for his passenger, *Fred*. The trip had already begun, but Fred had forgotten his wallet, and he's run back inside to retrieve it. It's trip #1 of the day and things aren't starting off too well.

With nothing better to do, Mark turns on the radio and patiently bides his time on the peaceful, empty street when suddenly a firestorm of honking rains down on him.

HONK-HONK-HOOOONNNNNNKKKKKK!!!

He looks in the side-view mirror and finds an SUV on his back bumper. A furious woman is mouthing curse words while waving her arms around like "Animal" from *The Muppets*. Now to be fair: Mark's car is not completely butted up against the curb—it's out an extra three feet—but there's still ample room to drive around. Unfortunately, such a slight maneuver appears to be an "end of the world" inconvenience for the woman, whose arm gesticulations have intensified...*Careful lady, you might pop a shoulder.*

HONNNNNNNNNKKKKKKKKK!!!!

Really?!

He casually sticks his arm out the window and waves for her to go around. Slowly the ponytailed soccer mom slides by. She stares him down, mutters under her breath, shakes her head...*I think she may be contemplating a drive by.*

She continues to cruise by at a snail's pace before easing in front of his car. As she does so, he notices a sticker on the rear window of the SUV. He leans forward to get a better look, wanting to make sure he's not misreading the message—he's not. In big, bold letters it reads:

NAMASTE

Immediately, his favorite line from *The Princess Bride* comes to mind...*You keep using this word. I do not think it means what you think it means.*

"REVERSE PSYCHOLOGY"

It's a Tuesday Night. Mark has gotten a request from *Keira.* He pulls up to a gated condominium complex, and a moment later a smiling, attractive, and well-dressed woman in her late 20s runs up to his car with short choppy steps so as not to stumble in her high heels. As she opens the back door, she tugs upwards on her strapless dress to make sure she's covered.

KEIRA: Mark?
MARK: Hey, Keira.
KEIRA: I hope you didn't have to wait too long.
MARK: No, I'm good.
KEIRA: Great. I'm running a little late.
MARK: Yeah, I can see that. You look like you're still getting dressed.
KEIRA: (laughing) I know. It's so embarrassing. I'm meeting up with some new co-workers, and I don't want to be late.
MARK: I get it. I'll get you there as soon as I can.

She smiles and Mark swipes the app, revealing a twenty-minute trip to Burbank.

MARK: So, Keira, I hear an accent in your voice, but I always get Scottish and Irish confused. I'm not even gonna guess.
KEIRA: Irish.
MARK: See there? I would have said Scottish.

She laughs.

MARK: How long have you been in the States?
KEIRA: Just a couple of months. I came here for work.
MARK: Yeah? What do you do?
KEIRA: International law.
MARK: Okay, good for you. How do you like L.A. so far?
KEIRA: I like it…but…
MARK: …*But??*
KEIRA: I'm wondering if I can meet a man here.

Mark laughs and Keira joins in.

KEIRA: I don't want this to come across the wrong way, but are there any good men in Los Angeles? They seem a bit shallow to me.
MARK: (laughing) Yeah, Los Angeles can certainly be a tough place to date, but I'm sure there are plenty of good men out there.
KEIRA: I hope so. I'd like to meet someone.
MARK: Well, Keira: you're very pretty, I'm guessing quite bright—being an international lawyer and all—and you seem to have a very good sense of humor, so I'm sure you'll have plenty of opportunities. Whether you like the men behind those opportunities is a whole other subject.

She laughs again, and Mark's happy to be entertaining her. For the next few minutes he gives her the lowdown on dating in L.A. and how difficult it can be to meet down to Earth people.

KEIRA: Thanks for the information.
MARK: No problem.
KEIRA: You know, I've got to say: you don't seem like an everyday, ordinary Uber driver.
MARK: No? What's "an everyday, ordinary Uber driver" like?

KEIRA: I don't know. I just talking with you. You seem to have a great deal of wisdom.
MARK: Well, I'm not so sure about that. I think you may be confusing wisdom with opinionated.
KEIRA: No, it's wisdom. I can tell.
MARK: Well, thank you, Keira.
KEIRA: You're welcome…So, what's your story?
MARK: Me? I don't have much of a story.
KEIRA: No? Ever been married? Kids?
MARK: Nope, never was in the cards. I always wanted kids—I've got a strong paternal instinct—but nope, not to be.
KEIRA: Hmmmm? Are you gay?
MARK: Ha! No, not gay. Although, going by lack of a love life, I bet some of my friends think I'm in the closet.

Keira leans forward.

KEIRA: How old are you?
MARK: How old do you think I am?
KEIRA: Ummmm?…Forty-two?
MARK: Nope.
KEIRA: Younger?
MARK: Okay, you are becoming my all-time favorite person. I'm almost 50.
KEIRA: No! Really??
MARK: I cannot tell a lie.
KEIRA: And you've never been married or had kids?
MARK: Afraid not.

Mark would prefer to go back to talking about Keira's dating woes, but the questions continue.

KEIRA: Why?

MARK: Why haven't I been married?
KEIRA: Yeah.
MARK: Oh, I don't know. I guess I've always been very picky. Plus, it seems like whoever I've liked, hasn't been into me, and whoever has liked me, I haven't been into them.
KEIRA: Hmmmmmm? So, there's no one special in your life?
MARK: No, not really.
KEIRA: *No one?*
MARK: Well, there's this one woman, Daniella, that I've liked for a long time, but timing's never been right. Truth is, I just don't think she's ever been into me, which is too bad: We always have a good time together. It's been awhile, anyway. I don't even know the last time we spoke. I think it's been over a year.
KEIRA: Maybe the timing's right now. You should call…um—
MARK: —Daniella.
KEIRA: Right. Call, Daniella. You never know.
MARK: Nah, that ship has sailed. It's best that I don't cross that bridge.
KEIRA: I think that's a mixed metaphor.
MARK: You're right. See how bright you are?!

They laugh.

KEIRA: Well, you can't give up on everyone.
MARK: I know, but things just don't seem to work out for me when it comes to relationships. I even went through a stretch where I'd know a woman for a while, and when I'd finally get the courage to ask her out, she'd tell me she'd just started dating someone. And then like clockwork, she'd be engaged a few months later. It happened like five times in a row. I even thought about opening a business to get lonely ladies hitched: I'd pretend to ask out the woman, and within months, she'd have a ring on her finger.
KEIRA: (laughing) I think there's a movie like that.

MARK: Yeah, I think so. But for me it wasn't fiction; it happened all the time. Even the fact that we're having a nice conversation means you've got a 50/50 shot to meet the man of your dreams tonight.

Keira laughs a little louder.

KEIRA: You have that much power, huh?
MARK: It appears so.
KEIRA: Well, I'm guessing your situation is just some bad luck, that's all.
MARK: Whatever. I'm over it. Besides, I've got more issues than a box of tissues.
KEIRA: "More issues than a box of tissues?" Like what?

Mark looks in the rearview mirror, Keira is staring at his reflection... *Ah, shit. You had to say that, didn't you?*

MARK: Nothing. I was just joking.
KEIRA: No, come on. We all have issues. What are yours?

His mouth quivers; he tries to keep his smile.

MARK: Aren't we supposed to be figuring out how to get you a man?
KEIRA: Not anymore. You're the subject now. What are your issues?

Again, his mouth quivers. His smile leaves him. He takes in a deep breath.

MARK: Ummm?...All right. You really want to know?
KEIRA: I do.
MARK: Okay, what the heck, I'll tell you. Besides, you'll be out of my car in another ten minutes, so I'll never see you again, anyway.

KEIRA: Wonderful. I'm listening.

He takes in another deep breath, exhales, then lets it rip.

MARK: So, I've always been wound pretty tight—that's not exactly a secret to me or anyone who knows me—but about a dozen years ago, I was out playing golf, and I got paired up with two older guys. At one point, one of them made a putt, and I picked up the ball so he didn't have to bend down. When I handed it back to him, our fingers grazed, and my body completely locked up.
KEIRA: What do you mean?
MARK: I don't know exactly; it was like I went into rigor mortis.
KEIRA: Oh my goodness.
MARK: Exactly. Anyway, it subsided after about a minute, but I was freaked out; the incident sat in my head for days.
KEIRA: I bet.
MARK: So, I started to monitor myself. And when I did, I realized that I'm *always* in a guarded state—not to the level of what happened on the golf course—but my muscles, especially my core, are constantly clenched. Even if I lie down and try to concentrate on relaxing, I can't. It feels foreign to me. Can you believe that?—Being tense feels more natural to me than being relaxed.
KEIRA: Oh, wow.

He attempts to lift the weight from the conversation.

MARK: I bet you weren't expecting all of this.
KEIRA: No, it's okay. It's fascinating. So, how does it affect you?
MARK: Well, I began to realize that unsuspecting or heightened affection *really* makes me tense.
KEIRA: Like you can't even hug a friend?
MARK: No, I can. I can give someone a hug or shake a stranger's hand. But if something unexpected arises: a longer, tighter hug

than usual, or even if a stranger walks by and smiles and says hello unexpectedly, I lock up pretty badly.
KEIRA: Wow. Did you ever try therapy?
MARK: I did.
KEIRA: And what happened?
MARK: The therapist's first question was, "Have you ever been molested?"
KEIRA: And?

They stop talking for a moment; Mark squirms in his seat.

MARK: ...I don't know. I have no memory of anything ever happening—I'm probably just wired this way—but there's been some patterns and incidents in my life that make me wonder. I remember one time when I was thirteen, I was at the doctor's getting a physical. I had just started going through puberty and I was lying on the examination table. He wanted to see how things were "developing." Well, the moment he lifted the front of my underwear, I started breathing erratically—almost to the point of hyperventilation.
KEIRA: Ohhh...
MARK: He did nothing wrong, but something bothered me. I never told anyone, and I pretty much forgot about it. But after what happened on the golf course, I started looking back, and that was one of those moments where I now wonder why I had such a strong reaction and if something had possibly happened along the way. I even remember my mom saying to me once, "You were so confident as a little boy, and then you suddenly changed."

Keira sits back, digests what she's heard. But while Mark was uncomfortable when he first started talking, he now feels some weight being lifted; he wants to continue.

MARK: Anyway, I've tried all sorts of ways to get to a better place: anxiety drugs, hypnosis—everything—but nothing's worked. I've pretty much avoided dating since that day on the golf course.
KEIRA: Hmmmm? I would think being aware of the problem would help—like you could stop the feeling when it comes on.
MARK: Yeah, you'd think, but the tension sneaks up on me so quickly and formidably that I can't seem to. In fact, the more I'm aware of it, the worse it gets.
KEIRA: Like a self-fulfilling prophecy?
MARK: Yep…And don't get me wrong, I have the desire to be with someone, but it's easier to simply side-step intimacy all together. I mean no woman wants a "science project," and people usually can't understand what I'm going through. They always say, "Just relax." I wish it was that easy. Sometimes I even wonder if over the years I've subconsciously self-sabotaged myself to avoid uncomfortable situations.
KEIRA: I see what you mean.
MARK: And there you have it, Keira: no marriages, no kids. Most of my friends don't even know about any of this. Honestly, I'm not sure why I opened up so much to you.
KEIRA: It's okay. Like I said, we're all humans. We all have our own thing.

Her comment makes him sit up a touch.

MARK: Yep, I suppose you're right: Everyone does have their own thing.

They pull up to her destination.

KEIRA: Ya know, I really enjoyed talking with you. We should grab a coffee together some time. Can I get your number?
MARK: Um…Yeah, sure.

He reaches down to grab one of his photography business cards, but as he does so, he notices his hand shaking...*Shit. Relax. Just relax.*

He smiles and reaches towards the backseat to give her the card—all the while, praying she doesn't notice his quivering hand.

MARK: Here ya go.
KEIRA: Great. Thanks for the ride and conversation. I'll give you a call.
MARK: Okay. I'll talk to you then.

Keira exits the car with a wave and a smile; Mark drives away with his head shaking.

She is so meeting her husband at that bar tonight.

"Astonishing"

★★★★★

“I’M ON THE PLANET!”

It’s 5 PM and Mark has just left a casting office in Santa Monica. When he gets to his car he decides to drive for a little while. He’s found that “Uber-ing” after an audition is a terrific way to get out of his head.

Anyone who’s spent even a decent amount of time in L.A. can spot post-audition actors from a mile away: no sense of others around them, head down, mouth going a mile a minute as they continuously repeat the dialogue they had just delivered at the casting office.

The small window of time spent at casting can be very stressful and is often reduced to a thirty-second—“my career and life is on the line”—pressure packed moment. Even simple dialogue—“He’s over there, Officer!”—can be nerve racking…*Did I put enough emphasis on “officer”?...* An actor’s world is all about making every opportunity count, because the next audition may be days, weeks, or even months away.

Fortunately, Uber has helped him get out of the post-audition “I should have done it this way” funk; tonight is no different. He prompts the app, and soon thereafter a request comes in from *Rachel,* who is on Pacific Coast Highway…*On PCH? Ugh, not good.*

He knows that finding Rachel will be a difficult task: There's nowhere to pull over or to turn around on PCH, and specific landmarks—gas stations and restaurants, for example—are rare. It's beach and very expensive homes for miles.

He looks at the app and sees the pick-up address...*600-700 Pacific Coast Highway? That's not very helpful, Uber. Well, let's go find her.*

After making his way down to the highway, he finds the 600-700 addresses and slides into the median lane. There's no sign of Rachel. He decides to call her.

RACHEL: Hello?
MARK: Hi Rachel, it's your Uber driver. I'm just trying to figure out your exact location. The address that came up says "600 to 700 PCH." Can you help me out?
RACHEL: Yeah, I'm at the beach.

He takes in her answer, blinks three times.

MARK: Uhhhh...Well, the beach is a pretty big area, Rachel. Can you be more specific?

She sighs.

RACHEL: I'm on The PCH!!!

He closes his eyes. His brain explodes.

First of all, no one calls PCH, "*The PCH.*" And secondly...Well, there is no *secondly*. He doesn't need a *secondly!* It's all ridiculous!

MARK: Ohhhh! Okay, Rachel. You're on *The PCH?* Just give me a moment; I'll be right there.

He reaches for his phone, cancels the trip, turns off the app, and immediately heads to nearby Westwood. There, he buys a ticket to the UCLA basketball game. Once inside, he finds his cousins who have season seats, and they all soon get their tickets upgraded by a generous UCLA marketing executive...*Sweet!*

The game is exciting, UCLA wins convincingly, and Mark hasn't thought about his audition one single time.

As he walks back to his car—a content hop to his step—he smiles towards the heavens...*Thanks, Rachel. You made my night. I hope you eventually found a ride home from "The PCH."*

**"Smart, personable driver.
Remarkable price."**

"NOTE TO SELF: WEAR HOCKEY MASK"

It's 10 o'clock on a Thursday night. Mark has just pulled up to a bar in East Hollywood to pick up *Sergei*. The crowd outside is rambunctious; patrons are sloppily spilling out the front door. Sergei soon exits. He's a big guy: around 6'3", 225 pounds. He's wearing a worn t-shirt and mid-thigh high white shorts that look like a cross between a bathing suit and boxer briefs. His hair is short and thinning. A manicured beard etches his face...Oh, and he's drunk. *Very drunk.*

He opens the passenger door and gets in. While Mark usually prefers riders to sit in the front seat because they tend to be friendlier and more courteous, Sergei is different. His inebriated state is obvious and immediately raises red flags...*The angry drunk: how wonderful.*

Within seconds—and without provocation—Sergei stares menacingly at him. His light blue eyes are icy, his lips are turned down. But Mark's not too concerned: He seems to have a knack at finding people's soft spot. Confidently, he swipes the app and sees they are heading to Silverlake...*Only twelve minutes. You got this.*

Unfortunately, it doesn't take long for him to realize that he'll need his full arsenal of diplomatic skills when it comes to Sergei, who immediately dives into Lake Asshole.

SERGEI: Let me guess: I bet you want to be a writer.

Mark smiles to keep things light.

MARK: Nah, maybe back in the day. I'm an actor.
SERGEI: *Pfffffft.* Who the fuck would want to be an actor?
MARK: Um, I guess me.
SERGEI: It's stupid. Actors are stupid. Why would you want to do it?
MARK: I don't know; I guess I've always enjoyed entertaining people.
SERGEI: Fuckin' stupid! A waste of time! Fuckin' stupid actors!

Oh boy.

As they stop at a red light, Mark leans forward and crosses his arms on top of the steering wheel. He's tired and really isn't in the mood for such B.S. His expression reveals as much... *What do you want, dude?*

Sergei mocks his arm placement.

SERGEI: Oh, so now we're all posing and shit!

Oh for fuck's sake.

The light turns green. Mark shakes his head and snorts out a breath of displeasure... *Just stay calm. Keep the tone of your voice as non-confrontational as possible. Maybe flip the subject.*

MARK: So, what do you do, Sergei?
SERGEI: I'm an agent.
MARK: Wait; you have a job that deals with actors?
SERGEI: Yeah, and they're idiots! Can't wait to be done with it.

MARK: Then why not do something else?
SERGEI: I will be.

Mark shakes his head. Sergei leans towards him.

SERGEI: You think you're pretty smart, don't you?
MARK: Nope. After all, I'm an actor, how smart can I be?
SERGEI: You know what? How-would-you-like-it-if-I-laid-my-seven-incher-across-your-forehead?

!!!

From the start of the trip, Mark had guessed Sergei to be gay, but now his instincts have been verified. Unfortunately, Sergei's announcement as to where he'd like to put his member has come across as a threat and not just a harassing moment.

Fuck, this is not good. Okay, think this through. Maybe pull over and tell him to get out. Or will that exacerbate the situation?...Shit... Probably safer to just deal with him and get him to his destination.

While Mark believes he can handle the situation, it's the first trip he's had where he's feels an altercation might occur...*Okay, be careful at a red light; he might try to sucker punch you...Man, I wish he was in the backseat. The distance would be safer...Shit... Just stay quiet. Don't say a word. It will work itself out.*

Unfortunately, Sergei is in no mood to be cordial; his agitation intensifies, and he begins swinging his arms around demonstratively.

SERGEI: What? You're not into it? Come on!

Mark's head shakes back and forth, although he tries to keep his displeasure as stealth as possible. However, as Sergei continues to flail his arms about, his left hand grazes Mark's arm. The moment there's contact, Mark's body locks up. A burst of adrenaline swims through his veins.

MARK: *Hey!!*—Don't fuckin' touch me again!! Ya got that?!

Silence and stillness take over, but Sergei does not stay quiet for long.

SERGEI: Ohhhhhh, soooo sensitive.

"Sensitive"—there's that fuckin' word. Don't push me, man. I'm the nicest guy in the world until I'm not.

He clamps his teeth together while navigating a narrow street in the hills of Silverlake. A minute later, he lands at Sergei's destination. He puts the car in park, freeing his hands to defend himself if need be. He looks over…*Well, get the fuck out!*…Sergei stares, fiddles with his keys, looks down, stares again…*You throw that punch you better be ready to kill me because I'm swingin' to the fuckin' death, you piece of shit.*

What is probably fifteen seconds of actual time feels like five minutes.

Sergei takes one last look and then exits the car.

Before the door is completely shut, Mark peels out.

MARK: *FUCK YOU, MOTHERFUCKER!!!*

Twenty minutes later, he steps into his apartment and makes a beeline to the tequila bottle in the freezer. He opens it and takes a swig... *Yo, God! I know I'm agnostic and all, but this would be a really good opportunity to show me you're out there. I'm begging you to give me that big break so I don't have to deal with idiots like Sergei any longer*...He takes another swig... *Yeah, probably not how this whole cosmic thing works, huh?*

He paces back and forth. Fixes a drink; downs it. Fixes another. He looks to his phone and wishes Keira would call. He just wants someone new in his life to give him a spark. It doesn't have to be romantic, even a new friend would be great. Plus, he's already spilled his guts to her, so everything's out in the open... *Shit. I should've gotten her number...* He scrolls down his contacts—stops.

Ah, why the hell not?

Even though it's been a year since they've spoken—and against his better judgement—he calls the one woman he really wants to be with: *Daniella.*

The phone rings four times and then goes to voicemail. He slaps his forehead... *Why? Why? Why?!—did you call??!*...He looks at his empty glass... *Stupid tequila.*

Beep

MARK: Hey—um—it's Mark. Surprise!!! You popped into my head and I thought I'd give you a buzz and say hi...Um, hi!...So, uh, anyway, hope all is well. Give me a call sometime if you get a chance.

He hangs up and slaps his forehead again. Drink #3 is fixed.

He tosses and turns all night, barely sleeps a wink.

At 3 AM he whispers into the darkness.

MARK: Yo, Dad, you out there?…I'm really not sure what to do any longer. Just had my best acting year ever and I still need to drive thirty hours a week just to make ends meet…Dad?…Dad?… Come on, Pop, give me a sign, an answer.

No answers come, and when the sun rises the next day so does Mark. He forces his way out of bed and starts the monotonous routine all over again—this time with a hangover and an extremely bitter taste in his soul.

"What a professional! I hope you succeed in acting!"

★★★★★

"OH, YOU MEAN ME"

Mark picks up two early twenty-something ladies in Koreatown. They are in a festive mood.

WOMEN: Hiiiiii!
MARK: Hi. Emily, right?
EMILY: Yep.
MARK: Cool. There's a lot of foot traffic; I just wanted to be sure I had the right person.
EMILY: Yep, it's me.

The women buckle up and begin telling stories.

EMILY: I got in the wrong car one time. It took me five minutes to figure it out.
FRIEND: I once requested a ride, and the app showed a woman would be picking me up. But when I got in, I saw that the driver was a man. I asked him if I was in the right car. He knew my name, so I stayed.

They laugh and continue to try to outdo one another.

EMILY: I was in a pool once and this elderly couple got in the car. They didn't know what a pool was, and they were like, "What are you doing in here?" And I was like, "It's a pool." They were old

and didn't understand. They started yelling at me, even called me a bitch.
MARK: Wait?! What???
EMILY: Yeah, and the driver didn't say a thing to these old people. Just kept letting them yell at me.
FRIEND AND MARK: What????
MARK: That's crazy.
EMILY: Right?! They were like forty or fifty, so I guess they didn't understand.

!!!!

Mark feigns pulling over.

MARK: I'm going to have to ask you ladies to get out of my car.
EMILY AND FRIEND: What?! Why?!
MARK: You said those people were "*elderly,*" and then said, "*They were like 40 or 50.*"

Immediately, the women get it and laugh.

EMILY: No, no, no. I just meant they were a *little* older.
MARK: You said "elderly" and "old people."

All three laugh a little louder. Eventually, Emily calms down.

EMILY: If you want to avoid traffic and not make a left, you can just drop us off on the right.
MARK: Nah, I got you guys. After all, us elderly folk got to take care of you youngins.

They giggle some more. Mark pulls up to their destination.

EMILY: I am so sorry. I really didn't mean it like that.
MARK: Not a problem; it was funny. You guys have a good night.

The backdoor is shut. Mark shakes his head.

"Old people, like forty or fifty"...Sheee-it.

"You are a wonderful, awesome, and amazing, YOUNG man."

"I'M SPEECHLESS"

JANUARY 20TH, 2017 - PART 1

Mark rolls over in his comfortable, warm bed and resettles. He lies still for a few moments, soaking in the last bit of slumber. Then suddenly, as if attached to surging electrodes, his eyes open, his muscles squeeze, and he springs into an upright position.

Holy shit, I'm 50!

The milestone birthday is hard for him to digest. He doesn't feel fifty—or whatever that chronological number is supposed to represent...*How am I fifty? This isn't possible*...Perhaps his half-hearted disagreement with his birth certificate is because he really hasn't lived: no travel, no serious relationships, no wild adventures...*I should still be fourteen with all of life ahead of me.*

He laughs at the notion while reflecting on his life—what he's accomplished, the world he's built for himself. He has regrets—doesn't everyone? But he also knows he's fortunate...*You're healthy, you've got great friends, and you're living in a dynamic city. This ain't so bad*...He smiles as he counts his many blessings.

Unfortunately, his content state does not last long; a moment later, another thought strikes him, and it strikes so forcefully, he instantly becomes nauseous...*Oh yeah, forgot about that.*

Turns out, the anniversary of his birth is not only a significant day in his life, but it's also significant on a national and international level. In fact, most of the world's eyes are focused upon the United States, specifically Washington D.C. It just so happens that Mark's birthday coincides with Inauguration Day, and in a few hours Donald and Melania Trump will take the keys to the White House from Barack and Michelle Obama…*On my friggin' 50*th*, no less. Ain't that a bitch?!*

While trying to push away any negative thoughts, he promises himself he'll avoid TV and social media and not let the events taking place in the Nation's Capital ruin *his* day. Instead, he plans to commemorate fifty years of life by celebrating all weekend long. Plus, in a few hours, he has his first audition of the year for a nice role on the biting comedy, *Speechless*. It's the second time he'll be reading for the part as the day before didn't go quite as planned…

Mark arrives at his audition more nervous than usual. As is customary, there's a kaleidoscope of butterflies filling his stomach, but on this day, a few wide-winged foes have also gotten stuck in his throat…Or at least so it seems.

The previous night, he attended his friend's son's high school basketball game. In what turned out to be one of the best games he's ever seen—a highly contested, overtime thriller in front of sold out gym—his cheering caused him to lose his voice. Now, as he's walking up to the *Speechless* casting office, the only sounds coming from his mouth are that of a twelve-year-old boy going through puberty.

He signs in, takes a seat next to the other auditioning actors, and hopes for a miracle. For the next ten minutes, he alternates between rehearsing his lines in his head and mouthing prayers to the acting gods.

A voice lifts him from his ping-ponged deliberation.

VOICE: Mark?

He looks up to see the casting director smiling at him.

He stands, smiles bashfully, and makes his way into the auditioning room.

CD: How are you doing today?
MARK: i'M fiNE, hOW ArE yOu?

The CD's eyes open wide; his eyes close.

CD: Um, are you okay?
MARK: No-O. I lOSt mY voICE LAst nIght.
CD: Oh no. Would you like to come back tomorrow?
MARK: COUld I?!
CD: Sure. I'm doing readings both days; it's no problem.
MARK: WoW, tHAnk yOU!

The moment he gets home he begins drinking tea and honey and doesn't stop for the rest of the day. By the time he heads to bed his voice is a little better but still not 100%. Then at 4 AM—the morning of his 50th birthday—he wakes and tries saying the dialogue…His voice is as good as new.

…As he's driving back to casting for his second chance, he feels maybe—just maybe—the universe is sending him some love. That feeling only intensifies when he finishes his last line in the auditioning room.

CD: Perfect! Very funny. It's a fun role, right?
MARK: It is. Once again, thank you so much for letting me come back.
CD: No problem.
MARK: Today's actually my birthday; this was a wonderful gift.
CD: Well, happy birthday. I'm glad it all worked out.

He leaves the office feeling very upbeat, knowing he nailed the read and has a good chance of booking the job.

After eating lunch, he attempts to take a nap, but he's pretty wound up. Between the audition, his birthday, and Inauguration Day, it takes an hour for him to relax and doze off. Within minutes of falling asleep he's dreaming of ducks.

QUACK!-QUACK!-QUACK!

He opens his eyes and realizes he's not dreaming—it's his phone's duck-ringtone, instead.

He thinks for a moment.

Wait! Oh, wait-wait-wait! Come on, please be Mariko.

He clutches the phone and looks to the screen.

No such luck. Instead, it's his best friend, Erik, calling from Northern California.

Erik—like most of Mark's close friends—refers to him as "Mudge." He was given the nickname as a baby, and the moniker has been around ever since. In fact, the name is used with such normalcy many people don't even know his real name; he's only known as "Mudge"...or "Mudgeopolis"...or "Mudgey"...or some other variation. Erik has his own version.

ERIK: Mudger Bloom! Happy birthday, my brother!
MARK: Thanks, E.
ERIK: What do you have planned for the big day? I know you're not watching what's happening in D.C.
MARK: Yeah, you got that right.

They laugh.

MARK: Well, I started the day with an audition.
ERIK: Cool, cool. What for?
MARK: *Speechless.* It went well. They start shooting on Monday, so I'm hoping to hear something this afternoon.
ERIK: That would be a great birthday gift.
MARK: No doubt.

Then, as if on cue, another call beeps in. He looks down and sees "Mariko" on the screen.

MARK: Yo, E, my agent is actually on the other line. Hang on one second.

He takes in a deep breath and lets it out slowly.

MARK: Hey, Mariko.
MARIKO: Yo, Mr. Bloom. How'd it go this morning?

His spirits drop—she's simply checking in to see how the audition had gone.

MARK: It went well. Wouldn't have done anything different.
MARIKO: Well, good, because you booked it!
MARK: *I booked it?!?*
MARIKO: You booked it!
MARK: Yesssssss!!!

Mariko releases her infectious laugh.

MARIKO: So, I'm assuming I can call them back and tell them you're available?
MARK: Uh, yeah, I think you can do that.

She laughs again

MARIKO: Well, congratulations, MB. You'll probably be getting a call from wardrobe and it shoots next week.
MARK: Awesome! Thanks so much.
MARIKO: You're very welcome…Oh! One other thing…
MARK: Yes??
MARIKO: Happy birthday, my friend. Have yourself a great day.
MARK: Thanks. I definitely will.

He hangs up and begins bouncing on the bed. But in his joyful state he almost forgets that Erik has been waiting on the other line.

MARK: E, you still there?
ERIK: Still here.
MARK: Sorry about that.
ERIK: No problem. Anything good?
MARK: As good as it can be; I got the role.
ERIK: You got it?!
MARK: I got it!

He sits back, smiling from ear to ear.

Even after so many years in the business he still finds himself in shock whenever he books a job (no matter how well an audition may have gone). With casting often receiving 2,000+ submissions per role, the odds of getting in the room, let alone beating out the other auditioning actors, is slim.

While Mark is excited, Erik is practically jumping through the phone.

ERIK: That's fantastic! I can't believe we were talking when it came through!
MARK: Yeah, pretty cool.
ERIK: Well, I hope that's just the beginning of a great birthday weekend for you, my brother. You better go celebrate tonight. Please tell me you're going out to celebrate.
MARK: Yeah, I've got some plans.
ERIK: Give it to me; whatcha got?
MARK: Well, I'm actually gonna go hang out with that girl, Daniella, that I've told you about.
ERIK: Remind me.

MARK: The one I've been interested in for years. She worked at that coffeehouse I used to go into. Remember?
ERIK: Oh, right! I thought you had stopped talking to her.
MARK: I did, but I was a little drunk the other night and I called her.

Erik chuckles.

ERIK: Doesn't it always start that way?
MARK: (laughing) Yeah, pretty much. Anyway—shockingly—she called me back. And since her birthday is next week, she suggested we get together and celebrate.
ERIK: Very nice! See this is what I like to hear: My boy books a job and has a date.
MARK: It's not a date. I just want to have a good time.
ERIK: I like it! You go have yourself a good time. Enjoy your night, enjoy your weekend, and I'll check-in with you next week.
MARK: Sounds good. Thanks for the call, E.
ERIK: No problem, my brother. Peace.
MARK: Peace.

They hang up and Mark is on cloud nine.

Soon thereafter, his day gets even better: Mariko calls back to tell him he's been booked for an extra day on *Speechless, and* they're giving him a weekly pay rate... *Wow! Maybe life truly begins at 50.*

Two hours later, he's standing outside, waiting with great anticipation for the Uber he ordered. And while he keeps reminding himself to not look forward, but simply enjoy the positive flow that the day has bestowed upon him, he can't help himself: he's excited to get across town and spend time with Daniella.

"MICKEY"

Mark prompts the Uber App and gets in his car for a late afternoon session. Within a minute, a request comes in. He heads down Cahuenga Blvd, looks to his left, and standing on the sidewalk—restless as can be, energy leaping from every pore of his body—is *Mickey.*

While waiting for traffic to break, Mark continues to view his soon to be passenger, and as he does so, a roaring river of memories flood his consciousness…

When Mark was growing up his two older brothers had lots of friends come over. They were all cool to him, but there was no one like Mickey. He was the perfect companion for Mark for one simple reason: he, too, was a sports junkie both on and off the court.

Mickey was also a great athlete, and whenever he'd come by, he'd take his little buddy out to the driveway and shoot hoops or pitch tennis balls to him for hours on end. He'd demonstrate Rod Carew's hitting style: opened up stance to free the hips and a lower resting bat angle to speed the hands through the hitting zone. Their sessions helped a little, and Mark smiled more than usual.

But, most importantly, Mickey lifted his confidence, especially when it came to basketball.

One day, an older neighborhood kid stopped by and Mickey was ready for him.

MICKEY: I'll bet you ten bucks you can't beat the Mudge in a game of *H.O.R.S.E.*

The older kid looked at the skinny, diminutive boy holding the basketball and did not hesitate to respond.

OLDER KID: Oh, you're on.

Fifteen minutes later, Mickey had a fresh ten-dollar bill in his hand, and he split the profits with his disciple.

During other visits, he'd quiz Mark on his sports knowledge.

MICKEY: Okay, Mudge, who was the 1958 American League Most Valuable Player?
MARK: Jackie Jensen.
MICKEY: (to no one in particular) I love this kid.

And Mark loved Mickey: He was like another brother.

However, when Mickey enrolled at a different high school, he pretty much disappeared. Still, Mark was able to follow his baseball career when he went on to play minor league ball. Once a week, the local newspaper would print the statistics of players from the Valley, and Mark would scour Mickey's stats, all the while remembering their times on the driveway.

Mickey got as far as playing Double A baseball before retiring, and Mark didn't see him again for another thirty years.

Then one day, while at a poker casino, he heard a voice from far away.

VOICE: Muddddddggggggge!

He turned, and there was Mickey—standing fifty feet away, bouncing around like a superball. Mark couldn't believe he had been recognized—the last time the two had seen each other he had been twelve years old.

Mickey was working as a chip runner at the casino that day and was running around like crazy, so the two didn't have time to sufficiently catch up. But one time in passing, he posed a question.

MICKEY: Hey, Mudge, who was the 1978 American League MVP?
MARK: You know I know the answer to that.
MICKEY: Of course you do. It was your all-time favorite player, Jim Rice.

Mark nodded with a smile.

MICKEY: See, I remember these things. You probably didn't think I would, but I do. *Jim Rice. The Mudge.* I remember.

Mickey then put his finger to his head as if to say, "It's all stored up here."

When Mark left that day, he found himself riding a teeter-totter of emotions. It was fantastic to see his old mentor, but Mickey also seemed different. He still had that fun, energetic spirit to him, but there was something else: it was as if life had hit him in the back of the head with the force of a Rod Carew line drive.

A few years later, they reconnected on Facebook but had no real communication. However, after moving to North Hollywood, Mark glanced at Mickey's page and saw he was managing a diner in the area. One evening, he dropped by unannounced. The moment the door swung open, Mickey turned, smiled, and released a *Mudddddddgggge!* hello that seemed to last an entire minute.

From then on, visits to the diner became a regularity. It was the perfect spot to get a good meal and talk sports for hours on end—each encounter a blast from the past.

Mark makes a U-turn and saddles up to the curb. Mickey gets in the backseat.

MARK: Hey, Mickey.
MICKEY: Mudge! Well, what do you know? I didn't know you were driving for Uber.
MARK: Yep, gotta do it.
MICKEY: I'm surprised. I keep seeing you on TV and thinkin', "Look at Mudge, he's a TV star."
MARK: Ha! Hardly.
MICKEY: Well, you haven't come into the diner for a bit. I figured you were running with a different crowd.
MARK: Never.
MICKEY: I know, I know, I'm just kidding with you. You're too good of a guy to forget where you came from.
MARK: Well, I haven't gone anywhere, anyway.

They laugh.

MARK: How are things going over there?
MICKEY: It's all I've got, Mudge. I go, I work, I come home; I watch a game, and then I do the same thing the next day. It's a boring life, but it is what it is.

Mark's suspicions from the casino thicken...*Something happened to him over the years.*

MICKEY: Hey, how's your brother?
MARK: I don't know. We don't really talk.
MICKEY: What? No?! Why?!
MARK: It's a lot of things. Don't get me wrong: I love him, I only want the best for him; he's got a lot of great qualities, but right now we're not in a good place.
MICKEY: I get it. You know your brother was a legend back in the day.
MARK: I know.
MICKEY: Nobody messed with your brother. I mean *nobody.*
MARK: I know.
MICKEY: One time there was this guy who thought he was tough shit. He was talking smack, and your brother didn't say a word. He just walked up, and you could tell he was pissed because—
MARK: —His jaw muscles were flexing.
MICKEY: Right! You could always tell when your brother was pissed because he'd clench his jaw. Anyway, the fight didn't even last fifteen seconds. Nobody messed with your brother. Nobody.

Mark is hoping the subject will change and Mickey soon obliges.

MICKEY: How's your mom?
MOM: She's doing pretty well.

MICKEY: Good. I love your mom. She was always so welcoming. Your house felt like home to me.

He laughs as a memory stirs.

MICKEY: Your brother would always mess with her. We'd be upstairs and he'd yell down, "Mom, Mickey wants you to make him a hamburger." I didn't ask for it, but your brother would say I did. And you know what she would do?—She would make me a hamburger! One time she even made a cake!!
MARK: Sounds like her.
MICKEY: Your mom is a saint. I love your mom. Please tell her I say hello. She probably won't remember me, but please tell her I say hello.
MARK: I will.

As quickly as Mickey gets to one subject, he's onto the next.

MICKEY: Hey, Mudge, do you also drive for Lyft?
MARK: No. A friend of mine has been trying to get me to, but I haven't yet.
MICKEY: Oh. All the waitresses at the diner swear by Lyft. They won't take Uber anymore. They say the drivers hit on them all the time.

This doesn't surprise Mark; he's heard some bad stories.

MICKEY: They say that Lyft drivers are much more professional.
MARK: I'm sure there's good and bad with both companies. I mean, look, I'm an Uber driver, and I'm a pretty good guy.

He winks; Mickey laughs.

MICKEY: True. You are. Hey, have you ever hit on a passenger?
MARK: Nah. I almost did once. I had this long trip with a woman; she was amazing: cool, smart, very good looking. We had a great conversation. She even worked at a sports network.
MICKEY: Wow, perfect.
MARK: Exactly. Anyway, we got to the end of the trip, and I wanted to ask her out so badly, but, nope, I couldn't pull the trigger.
MICKEY: Oh man, you should have.
MARK: Yeah, maybe. But then she'd probably end up talking smack about me just like the waitresses do.

Mickey laughs as they pull up to the diner.

MICKEY: Well, don't be a stranger, buddy. And this is for you.

He drops a crumpled up five-dollar bill onto the passenger seat.

MARK: No, Mickey, you don't have to do that.

Mark holds up the five and tries to hand it back, but Mickey's already halfway out the door.

MICKEY: Keep it. And tell your mom I said hello.
MARK: Thanks. I will.
MICKEY: Oh, one other thing—
MARK: Yeah?
MICKEY: —Who was the 1974 National League MVP?
MARK: Steve Garvey.
MICKEY: That's right! Mr. Forearms, himself. You still got it, Mudge. I'll see you soon.

As Mark watches Mickey take his place behind the counter—a long night still ahead of him—memories swell in the pit of his stomach…*You have yourself a good night, Mickey. You definitely deserve it.*

"Thanks, Mudge!"

★★★★★

"THE BED YOU MAKE"

Friday nights are meant for fun. It's the end of a long work week and people want to get out, be with friends, have a great meal, and maybe enjoy a drink or two. For Mark, a Friday night means he'll be driving these end-of-the-week revelers to their various happy spots. Admittedly, he sometimes gets jealous. All the laughing and high spirits, the conversations of what the night has in store, can get to him. But he knows "You sleep in the bed you make": he's got no one to blame for his decisions in life other than himself.

As he drops off his latest joyous passengers, he looks right and notices a couple exiting a restaurant. There's something familiar about them. He looks a little closer, and it registers: it's the parents of his old friend, Chuckie.

As a kid, Mark had an affinity for Chuckie's mom, whom he thought was extremely nice and welcoming. So, with a smile arching across his face, he double parks and steps out onto the street.

MARK: Well, if it isn't Mr. and Mrs. Jacobs.

They look over; there's no recognition.

MARK: It's Mark Bloom.

Still no recognition.

MARK: Mudge.

Mrs. Jacobs explodes with excitement, runs over, and gives him a big hug.

MRS JACOBS: Oh my gosh, Mudge! I haven't seen you in…
MARK: …In a long, long time.

They release their embrace and smile at one another.

MRS JACOBS: Have you seen Chuck at all?
MARK: Yeah, we reconnected not too long ago. Although to me, he'll always be *Chuckie.*

He winks, and Mrs. Jacobs keeps shaking her head in bemusement.

MRS JACOBS: I can't believe you recognized us.
MARK: Nah, you both still look the same. I was like, "That's Mr. and Mrs. Jacobs, I've got to say hello."
MRS JACOBS: I'm so glad you did. What are you doing with yourself?
MARK: Well, tonight I'm being an Uber driver.

He points to the sticker on his car.

She looks over, then swings her head back to Mark, and he sees it: her smile has dropped ever so slightly; there's a hint of disappointment in her eyes, and it's as clear as day. He knows that she's not being judgmental, it's just that almost everyone he grew up with now owns a home, has a steady job, is living a "normal life."… *They're probably even out and about enjoying their Friday night.*

Mrs. Jacobs sways back and forth; a surge of discomfort guides her movements. As best she can, she tries to keep her smile intact.

MRS JACOBS: Ohhhhh. So…uh…You're driving for Uber.

Mark smiles, not wanting her to feel uncomfortable.

MARK: I drive so I can keep pursuing my acting career.

She immediately perks up.

MRS JACOBS: Oh! So, you're doing what you want!
MARK: Yeah.
MRS JACOBS: Well, that's great!

His smile widens.

They catch up for another minute or two before he excuses himself.

MARK: Well, I better get back to it. It was great seeing you both.
MRS JACOBS: It was great seeing you too, Mudge. I'll tell Chuck—Chuckie—we saw you.
MARK: Great. Enjoy the rest of your weekend.

He waves goodbye, gets back in his car, buckles up, and taps the app. Within seconds, it chimes, causing his body to deflate. A muffled chuckle forces its way from his mouth…*Yes, Mrs. Jacobs, I'm doing what I want.*

"PERFECTO!"

JANUARY 20, 2017 - PART 2

Deep breath in...Exhale out...Deep breath in...Exhale out...

The same two thoughts keep circling around Mark's mind.

Deep breath in...Exhale out...Deep breath in...Exhale out...

After ten, calming minutes, his eyes open. Unfortunately, he's a bit startled when he finds his Uber driver, *Steve*, glancing at him in the rearview mirror.

STEVE: You okay?

He takes a mental scan of his body: There's an occasional jolt of tension, but he knows anxiety can strike a lot harder. He accepts his current state as a victory.

MARK: Yeah, I'm fine. Thanks.

Steve nods.

MARK: I apologize—I usually sit in the front seat. I drive, too, and I like conversation. I'm just trying to concentrate on something.

Steve nods again.

STEVE: No problem, man.

As they head out of the Valley, over the hill, and into Culver City, Mark thinks back to the first time he saw the person responsible for his present state of anxiety—Daniella…

It's been near fifteen years now since he walked into a neighborhood coffeehouse and spotted the cute barista standing behind the counter.

As he looks out the window of the Uber, he remembers how he was immediately attracted to her and how she introduced him to a traditional Mexican pastry called a "chamuco," professing that someday she would own her own coffeehouse, featuring Mexican desserts "like the world has never seen." And while he thoroughly enjoyed the chamuco, he was much more interested in the smiling woman, with the big brown eyes and cute, curvy body—Daniella.

From that day forward, he'd stop by the coffeehouse as often as possible, slowly nibble on a chamuco, and hope to catch Daniella on her break so they could hang out for a bit. But for years, other than some innocent flirting, nothing ever happened between them. Eventually, however, they began to spend some time together and had a brief, innocent romance. He still remembers the first time they kissed—it was awful. It was sloppy and wet, like two overeager puppies trying to show affection for one another and failing miserably.

The memory draws a tiny smile to his face, but it's short lived as he also remembers how horrifyingly nervous he had been: His left leg bounced uncontrollably; his hands shook like leaves in a hurricane. For the longest time he thought he'd never get past the onslaught of tension that would attack his body whenever they were together.

Then, one night, he finally felt at ease. It was the first time he had truly felt comfortable with someone. His calm state may have been because Daniella had some intimacy issues of her own, and it gave him some peace of mind, knowing he wasn't the only "freak" in the world.

Unfortunately, his breakthrough was short lived—Daniella soon committed to a long-distance relationship, and he was left out in the cold.

However, the two remained friends and occasionally would get together for dinner, where they'd flirt and reminisce about old times. But as time went by, Mark found himself more and more attracted to her, and he couldn't help but wonder what they'd be like together.

There were a couple of instances where he felt the stars were aligned—she was single, both of their lives were in a good place, they lived close to one another—but still nothing happened.

Each time it left him disappointed. However, he often wondered if his attraction to her was simply because he had finally found someone that he felt physically comfortable with, and starting from scratch seemed daunting. But he knew that wasn't the case because no matter what they would be doing, as long as he was with her, he would be enjoying himself.

* * *

...As the car stops in front of the coffeehouse that Daniella recently purchased, he makes a promise to himself...*Just have fun tonight. Don't think. Just have fun.*

He pulls out a five-dollar bill, hands it to Steve.

STEVE: Thanks. Enjoy your night.
MARK: I'm definitely gonna try.

He looks through the front window of the coffeehouse and spots Daniella. He monitors himself again: he's relaxed—at least relatively speaking...*Atta boy; you're doing fine. If you get anxious, just think about that stress-free night you spent with her. You're good, buddy.*

He takes in one last deep breath, lets it out slowly, then strides forward.

As he enters, he's taken back to the moment he first saw her. His heart pumps a little faster.

MARK: Hey there.

She turns and smiles.

DANIELLA: Hey! So good to see you!
MARK: Great to see you too.

They hug for a moment before she spins around with her arms extended.

DANIELLA: So, this is it! What do you think?
MARK: It's very cool. You did it. All these years talking about getting your own place and you made it happen. I'm very impressed.
DANIELLA: Thanks. It needs a lot of work, but I have a bunch of ideas; it'll get there.
MARK: I'm sure it will.
DANIELLA: Oh, I almost forgot, I have something for you.

She grabs a small, circular wrapped gift.

DANIELLA: Here ya go.
MARK: I think I know what this is.

He pulls back the bundled tissues to find three chamucos.

MARK: My favorite.
DANIELLA: We'll eat them later...If you want to share, of course.
MARK: Yeah, maybe.

He winks, she paws at his arm, and they're off.

They first stop at a local happy hour and begin catching up. Mark tells Daniella about moving back to the Valley, the acting successes he had the previous year, and the *Speechless* booking from earlier in the day.

DANIELLA: Wow! Look at you! You're really doing it.
MARK: Trying.

As they continue to bring each other up to speed on their respective lives, Mark can't stop smiling. Each have made dramatic changes since they first met, and while he isn't expecting anything to happen between them—nor is he trying—he still feels much more alive in her presence.

Halfway through drink number two, his appreciation for her multiplies.

DANIELLA: Oh, besides the coffeehouse, you know what else I did this last year?
MARK: No, what?
DANIELLA: I started playing fantasy football.

He practically falls off his chair.

MARK: Stop it!
DANIELLA: What?
MARK: STOP IT!!!
DANIELLA: WHAT?!?

He shakes his head and sits back to get a full view of her.

MARK: You're perfect. You're smart, you're fun, you're easygoing, you're beautiful, you're sexy, you've got your own business, and now you're playing fantasy football?!—Yep, you're perfect.

Daniella laughs and puts her hand on his thigh. Meanwhile, Mark isn't joking—he thinks she's perfect.

DANIELLA: Where are we going to next?!

He suggests a high-end bar by the beach. She lifts her eyebrows.

DANIELLA: Come on, you know I don't need any of that fancy stuff. Let's go find a dive bar.

Yep, you're perfect.

They find one nearby, order more drinks, and begin to flirt. Daniella suggests they snuggle for a selfie to recreate a picture from another dual birthday celebration, years earlier. She posts the photo to Instagram, adding the caption *#welookgood.* He doesn't disagree.

DANIELLA: What now?
MARK: I know, let's go dancing.

She nods.

The first place they try is closed, but soon they make their way to a bar that has a small dance floor. It's loud and dark, and they both have had their fair share of drinks. They never make it to the dance floor. Instead, they move to the rhythm of the music just off to the side. She teases him, pressing her body to his, their lips almost touching. He, however, just keeps dancing. He's been down this road with her before…*If you want a kiss, then kiss me…* Soon thereafter, she does just that. It's the first time they've kissed in years, and it's not a sloppy mess like the first time; it's soft and sensual and sexy.

An hour later, they are in an Uber heading to her apartment. When they arrive, her attention shifts to her two little dogs. She takes them out to pee before she, Mark, *and the dogs* settle in.

DANIELLA: Do you want to spend the night?

MARK: Yeah, I can.
DANIELLA: I mean on the couch.

He looks down at the two pups who think they're going to have a new friend to cuddle with.

MARK: You're not even going to let me sleep in your bed? It's not like anything has to happen.
DANIELLA: I just feel uncomfortable with my roommate here.

The dogs whine.

MARK: Well, I really don't feel like sleeping on a couch with your dogs, and my oldest brother is coming in town early tomorrow, so it's probably best if I just head home.

Fifteen minutes later, he's in an Uber on his way back to his apartment. During the ride he recounts his 50th birthday—*Speechless*, Trump, calls from friends and family, his time with Daniella. He's exhausted, thrilled, frustrated, and alive. It's been quite a day. Plus, he still has a weekend full of plans, an acting job the following week, and perhaps (*perhaps!)* the start of something with Daniella…*I mean, my goodness, she plays fantasy football. She's perfect!*

When he wakes the next morning, he sends her a text, thanking her for such a fun evening. A couple of hours later, his brother, Jeff, gets in town, and they head out to Westwood for the UCLA-Arizona basketball game. Despite a disappointing Bruin loss, the atmosphere is electric, and they have a great time bonding. That night, they go out for Sushi, then step over to the dive bar next door to meet up with a few friends. The festivities are capped the following morning when Mark's joined by family and some of his oldest and dearest friends for brunch.

After Jeff takes off that evening, he collapses on his couch and calls Daniella but only gets her answering machine.

MARK: Hey. Just seeing how your weekend was. Hit me back when you can.

He doesn't hear from her over the next few days, and his disposition diminishes with each passing minute. His only saving grace is two fantastic days working on *Speechless*. The cast and crew are terrific, the scenes play well, and his rapport with the director is wonderful.

She approaches him after his final take.

DIRECTOR: You were fantastic. I hope we get to work together again someday.
MARK: Me too. Thanks for having me.

He leaves the set feeling like a true professional. But as he walks to his trailer, all he can think about is Daniella and how great it would be to have someone at home to celebrate with. He's certainly happy about his professional success, but sitting alone on his couch, eating popcorn, watching basketball highlights on *Sportscenter*, isn't exactly his dream scenario.

Upon stepping into his trailer, he checks his phone and shockingly finds a missed call from her. He quickly changes clothes, signs out, and says goodbye to the production team.

Once in his car, he calls her.

DANIELLA: Hey.
MARK: Hey, how are you?
DANIELLA: I'm good. You?
MARK: Great. Just leaving set. It was a lot of fun.
DANIELLA: That's great. Um, listen, I need to talk to you.

She pauses. Mark prepares himself for her next words.

DANIELLA: I was drunk the other night. I shouldn't have kissed you. I'm sorry if I gave you the wrong impression.

Surprisingly, his heart *doesn't* sink. Instead, he smiles a frustrated smile and releases a quick sighing laugh.

MARK: Yeah, I kinda had a feeling you were going to say that.
DANIELLA: I'm sorry. Honestly, it was one of the most fun nights I've ever had. Definitely the most fun I've had in a long, long time.

This statement, however, *makes* his heart sink…*I know! We are great together! We always have fun! We're good for each other! What is the problem???*

They talk for a few more minutes, but his thoughts have drifted.

DANIELLA: Let's get together soon. We'll go hit up a happy hour.
MARK: Huh?…Um, yeah…Okay, yeah. Sounds good.

They hang up.

He's like a zombie on the way home. All the good things from the previous week have been squashed by Daniella's latest dismissal.

He blames himself for much of it, knowing she probably never had any real interest in him, anyway.

When he gets home, he throws a bag of popcorn in the microwave, flips on ESPN, and spreads out on the couch. The sports highlights are a blur in the background. He stays in his head and tries to find ways to soften the disappointment...*Not every story has a happy ending, ya know. Look at how much fun you had working on Speechless. Be happy with that. Just move on.*

But at that moment there is no way to spin his feelings. He shakes his head, and as he does so, a phrase births in his mind. He chuckles—though isn't sure why—as he thinks about the words that have melded.

I guess I'm waiting for my next life.

"Remember: 'The grass is always greener on the other side.' But sometimes when you get to that grass, you find out it's just AstroTurf."
—passenger

"IS THIS THING ON?"

It's a busy night in the heart of Santa Monica. Mark pulls up to the corner of Wilshire and Third Street. Before he knows it, a group of four college-age students pile in. He swipes the app and sees they are heading to Koreatown—a thirty-five-minute drive in mid-evening traffic.

The group is boisterous but friendly, and Mark quickly gets in their good graces when he finds out they attend Washington State University.

MARK: The Palouse!
LEAD GIRL: How do you know about the Palouse?
MARK: Every real college football fan knows Washington State is located on the Palouse. I've watched many a favored team squander away a fruitful season, at the hands of an upstart, determined Cougar squad, on a bone chilling November night on—
BACKUP SINGERS: —The Palouse!!!
LEAD GIRL: Wow! Impressive.
MARK: I'm no Grantland Rice, but I try.
LEAD GIRL: Who?
MARK: Grantland Rice. He was a very famous sports wri—

Mark looks over and quickly remembers just how big of an age gap there is between him and his passengers.

MARK: —Never mind. So, where have you guys visited during your trip?
LEAD GIRL: Griffith Park…
BACKUP SINGERS: ...Hollywood...LACMA...Venice...
LEAD GIRL: …The Museum of Broken Relationships.
MARK: You visited my apartment?

Silence.
More silence.
An uncomfortably palpable dead air of silence.

MARK: Sorry. Uber humor.

Laughter.
More laughter.
A thrilling—and surprisingly—large amount of spirited laughter.

The rest of the trip is very pleasant. Mark finds each of his passengers to be kind, easy to talk to, and courteous.

They arrive at the drop-off spot.

BACKUP SINGERS: Thank you…Thank you…Thank you.
LEAD GIRL: Yeah, thanks for the ride…And keep up the funny jokes.

Mark grins, turns off the app, and heads home. As he enters his apartment, he checks the night's totals. There, he finds a nice gift waiting: a $4 tip. His smile grows... *The Palouse!*

"Mark is personable, funny and definitely knows LA!"

★★★★★

"UBER IMPRESSED"

It's early afternoon. Mark has just gotten a request. Five minutes later, he pulls up to a North Hollywood apartment building, and out bounds *Yazmin.* He instantly finds her to be a delightful air of bubbly goodness. She struts with a purpose. Her caramel skin glows. Her smile is electric. And her hair?—Well, her hair is magnificent!—Giant! Full! An enormous soft mushroom of dark brown curls! She is the complete opposite of Mark, and his appreciation for her grows because of that very fact.

Yazmin gets in the front seat...*Nice. She's gonna be cool*...Her first words—while simple—only crystalize his premonition.

YAZMIN: Hey, Mark! Thanks for picking me up.

Her voice matches every aspect of her physical being—alive!

MARK: No problem. Where are we off to?
YAZMIN: I've got a commercial audition. I'm actually running a little late.
MARK: Oh shoot. Well, let's see if we can get you there as quickly as possible.
YAZMIN: Oh, don't worry; I'll be fine. It's one of those where you go in with your friends. It's actually a callback.
MARK: What? And you're running late?!

She exaggerates a grimace, showing no signs of panic.

YAZMIN: I know.
MARK: Look at you: You're so calm.
YAZMIN: It will be okay. It's just one audition…Excuse me for a second; I just want to call my friend to let her know that I'm running late.

As Yazmin makes her call, Mark thinks about how different she is than most actors he knows—including himself. Few would be as relaxed as her. Her attitude exudes confidence, declaring *she* is the product, and everyone will be thrilled when she enters the room. At the same time, she doesn't come across as arrogant or disrespectful. Instead, she simply knows that life doesn't always go as planned—*Sometimes you're just running late.* Plus—*It's just one audition; there will be more.* It's a quiet, respectful confidence she embodies.

After a quick, upbeat conversation with her friend, she re-engages.

YAZMIN: So, Mark, what do you do besides drive people all around town?
MARK: Oh, I do the L.A. nonsense thing too: I'm an actor and photographer.
YAZMIN: Yeah, I had a feeling.

Her infectious smile shines again, and he follows suit.

MARK: How are things going for you?
YAZMIN: Ya know, the typical highs and lows. I've got an improv group that I'm in, and I perform "spoken word" regularly.

Her mentioning of spoken word lifts Mark even higher. He's been a fan of the poetic art form for some time.

MARK: That's so cool. I actually just wrote my first piece.
YAZMIN: Well, look at youuuuuu!
MARK: Yeah, but I haven't had the guts to perform it yet.
YAZMIN: You need to!
MARK: I know, I know. One day I will. Hey, would you recite one of yours for me?
YAZMIN: Absolutely…But only if you do yours in return.

Yazmin's request is accompanied by a radiant smile that fills the car with light. Mark stares at her, practically hypnotized…*Uhhhhh?… You know what? Why not? You only live once.*

MARK: Yeah, okay.

Over the next couple of minutes, Yazmin performs one of her poems. It's magnificent. A flowing piece with dips and turns, highs and lows. The poem, based upon the strength of women, is artful and emotional. Mark is captivated not only by her words but also by her delivery and presence. She is a true artist.

MARK: Wow. That was amazing.
YAZMIN: Thank you. Okay, your turn.
MARK: I was hoping you had forgotten about that.
YAZMIN: Nope! A deal's a deal.
MARK: Indeed: a deal's a deal.

He proceeds to recite his poem with as much vigor as he can deliver. As he finishes the last verse, he finds himself sitting uncharacteristically tall and proud. It's only the second time he's recited the piece to anyone, the only other time having been to his budz, Kim.

But once the performance high has worn off, he realizes that a tangible silence has taken over the car. He can't look over and his spine curves to form a perfect comma.

For what seems like minutes, they ride in silence, but then—to his surprise and relief—a slow-clap rises from the passenger seat. He looks over. A glorious grin is engulfing Yazmin's face.

YAZMIN: Well, okay, Mark! That was really good. You need to get up on stage and let the world hear you.

He turns back to the road. A bashful smile sits just below his crimson cheeks.

MARK: Thank you.

The two exchange Instagram information, and he wishes her good luck at the audition—he has a feeling she's going to book the job. If it was up to him, he'd cast her in anything.

YAZMIN: Thanks for the ride. That was a lot of fun.
MARK: No, thank *you.* All the best with everything. I look forward to seeing your star rise.

They both smile then go their separate ways.

As he drives away, Mark knows Yazmin is a very marketable actress. He also knows that talent, looks, and even a great audition doesn't mean an actor will book a job. Sometimes, instead, the casting process is weighted quite differently. Many years earlier he saw this phenomenon up close and personal while working as a production assistant...

The tasks of a PA are a little all over the place: sorting and checking time cards, filing paperwork, picking up lunch, putting gas in the director's car—whatever the production team needs is done. Mark has been working as a PA for a company that produces commercials for a few years, and while he's old for the job, it allows him some flexibility, and the team is like a second family to him.

One of his steady assignments is setting up and breaking down callback sessions. TV shows usually move too fast to have callbacks, but commercials almost always do. Typically, the director goes through the videotapes of the first session, then narrows down the list of actors he or she wants to see again.

At callbacks, a whole slew of executives and higher-ups can be in the room: the director, agency producers, the clients, and many other talking heads whose jobs are hard to define. As an actor, Mark has walked into a room and found as many as a dozen faces staring back at him. Fortunately, the company he works with has a much smaller group—usually a handful of producers and the director.

One afternoon, he arrives at the tail end of a callback session to clean up and gather materials that need to go back to the production office. When he steps in the room, he finds the director and producers have already begun discussing their casting options. As he takes a seat of to the side and waits for them to make their decision, he finds a split room: Three producers are lobbying for one actress, two producers and the director are lobbying for the other.

Despite all of them liking both women, the debate rages on for another thirty minutes. Then, one of the weary producers half-jokingly makes a suggestion.

PRODUCER: Let's just toss their headshots up in the air. We'll go with whichever one turns face up.

!!!

Suddenly, an odd noise fills the room, and it has emanated from where Mark is sitting. The sound was most likely a gasp, but it's also possible that his chin literally unhinged itself from his jaw and hit the floor with a thud. No matter, all six higher-ups snap their heads to him in perfect synchronicity.

Wide eyed and shaking ever so slightly…*This is how a final casting decision can be made?!*…He is comforted by the producer.

PRODUCER: See? You can't take it personally. You never know what's going on in the room.

He nods but is still hoping they can find a better way to make their decision. Unfortunately, his wishes are not granted; the producer grabs the actresses' headshots, swings her hands high into the air, and lets her fingers unravel at their apex.

In what appears to be happening in slow motion—at least to Mark—the 8 x 10 photos float back down to the ground, twisting and turning through the air as if God himself is making the final choice. One headshot hits the floor with a *plop* and is turned face down. The other one floats easily; a bed of feathers seemingly await its arrival to help soften the landing.

When it meets the floor, it's turned right side up. The actress's lovely smile shines bright for all to see. Everyone circles round to see who the lucky winner is.

CASTING DIRECTOR: Yeah, give it to her. It would be her first commercial.

The choice is made.

As it turns out, the role is the first of many for the actress whose career steamrolls forward to bigger and better things—both in entertainment and on the world stage. The actress?—Meghan Markle. *Princess Meghan Markle.*

...As he swipes to accept another trip, Mark hopes that Yazmin's headshot is weighted properly. Somewhere down the line, he'd like to see her dazzling smile once more.

"You showed up early, which was greatly appreciated, and you gave me a fun ride. Be well!"

"SAY ANYTHING"

Mark pulls up to his pickup location in Studio City. He's hoping his passenger, *Tomas,* is waiting outside…No such luck. Instead, the street is quiet and uninhabited. There are no passersby, no dogs are being taken for walks, not even a curious squirrel is scampering about.

With his patience running thin, he eyes the front door of the apartment building…*Come on, Tomas, where are you?*...The door does not open.

Dammit, Tomas!! Come on!!!

There's a good reason for Mark's heightened anxiety: twenty-four hours earlier, he had picked up a passenger in a bus zone, only to be approached by a once-hiding police officer. Now the proud owner of a $293 ticket, he knows it will take two full days of driving to simply break even…*So let's go! This ticket ain't paying for itself!*

He slams his head back, looks to the opposite side of the street, and lo-and-behold there's Tomas standing motionless on the sidewalk. His shoulders are slumped, his face is tired and flat, his weathered fingers are gripping the handles of two old guitar cases that reflect his worn-out state. A ratty black trench coat drapes down his body. It sits atop a wrinkled black t-shirt, which sits atop a paunchy belly, which sits atop a pair of black jeans. The only thing breaking up the color palette is Tomas' blinding white skin and shoulder length bleached blonde hair, which has definitely seen better days. To Mark, he's a mash up of two prominent 1980s movie characters: "Lloyd Dobler" from *Say Anything* and "John Bender" from *The Breakfast Club—if* the characters had not taken care of themselves for thirty years and bleached their hair blonde... *Must be the trench coat.*

At a sloth's pace, Tomas makes his way to the trunk and methodically (or just slowly) places the guitar cases amongst a graveyard of audition sides before plopping down in the backseat.

Mark swipes. The destination is the world-famous music venue, *The Viper Room*. Going by Tomas' rock 'n' roll make-up, The Viper Room makes sense, but it's also confusing since it's 7:30 in the morning on a Tuesday.

MARK: Um, The Viper Room? Is that right?

Tomas answers as slowly as he moves.

TOMAS: No...no. Really that's what it says? No...no...no. I'm going to Silverlake.

This ticket is never going to get paid.

MARK: Well, I need you to enter the correct address before we can go anywhere.

Tomas fiddles and faddles with his phone.

TOMAS: Can you help me?

MARK: Yeah, sure.

He grabs the phone and finds the correct prompt.

TOMAS: Wowwww. Thanks. That was great.

Yeah, I'm a real friggin' magician, Tomas.

As their journey begins, Mark decides he's spent enough time worrying about the ticket, and the best way to get out of his stress filled head is through conversation.

MARK: So, you're a musician, huh?
TOMAS: Yeah.
MARK: That's cool.

Tomas shrugs.

TOMAS: Today's my day off.
MARK: Oh, um, okay…Good for you. What are you going to do with your day off?
TOMAS: (distant) Practice songs.

The statement seems a bit odd, but Mark doesn't want to push the subject.

MARK: I think my neighbor was the keyboardist for *Dio*, back in the day.

Tomas takes this in.

TOMAS: That's a good gig…Yeah, that's a good gig.

His voice trails off, but Mark hears an accent.

MARK: Where are you from?
TOMAS: Sweden, but I've been in Los Angeles for years.

Again, his voice withers at the end of his response.

MARK: I bet you've seen a lot of the world being a musician. Where's the best place you've ever been?
TOMAS: I like Deep Purple.

?

Mark looks in the rearview mirror. Tomas confidently looks back... *Was that a connection to Dio?*

Not being a music aficionado and beginning to realize that Tomas' brain isn't processing info at a speedy rate, he decides to repeat the question.

MARK: Um, do you have a favorite place that you've played? A country or city?
TOMAS: England...Scotland...I think I'll move back to Sweden...I hate L.A.
MARK: Really? Why is that?
TOMAS: Why is what?
MARK: Um...Why do you hate L.A.?

Tomas tries to formulate his reasons, but there's no structure to his words.

MARK: Don't worry; I won't be offended. I grew up here, but there's still a lot about L.A. that I don't like.

Tomas doesn't respond and Mark figures there's no reason to keep forcing the conversation. But then suddenly—at the exact moment they begin taking a GPS led shortcut through Griffith Park—a dollar bill is slapped on the middle counsel between the two front seats.

TOMAS: This is for you, Mark. It's all I've got on me.
MARK: Well, thanks, but don't you want to wait until the end of the trip?

Tomas doesn't say a word. Instead, he sits back with a thud and gazes longingly out the window.

TOMAS: It's beautiful out here.
MARK: Yeah, it really is. I've actually never been through this section of the park.
TOMAS: Really?...Well, don't hit a deer.
MARK: Ha! Yeah, I'll do my best.

With glazed eyes, Tomas' continues to stare vacantly at the landscape, but a hint of life seems to be surfacing. Mark even believes he sees a tiny grin forming...*I bet he'd like to jump out of the car and roll around on the dewy grass for hours on end.*

Ten minutes later, they arrive in Silverlake and stop in the middle of an empty restaurant parking lot.

MARK: Is this the right place?

Tomas nods, seemingly crestfallen to the core.

The trunk is popped. Mark steps out of the car to help retrieve the guitars.

MARK: Only if you need a hand, Tomas. I don't want to touch the valuable equipment.

Tomas looks to him. He suddenly becomes extremely focused.

TOMAS: They're just guitars.
MARK: Yeah, but you've made a living with them. I bet it's cool being a professional musician.

Tomas looks away. His face scrunches as he tries with all his might to conjure up some good times.

Seconds later, his face lengthens back to its original form.

TOMAS: It's okay.

Mark nods. Tomas has definitely seen a thing or two...*Rock 'n' Roll, baby.*

MARK: You take care of yourself, okay?
TOMAS: Yeah...Thanks...You too.

Then, unhurriedly—and without clear direction—Tomas meanders across the parking lot: a downtrodden, paunchy, bleach blonde, Lloyd Dobler/John Bender mashup, who doesn't appear ready to raise a boombox above his head in order to win over his love nor put his fist in the air in defiant victory, anytime soon.

Rock 'n' Roll, baby.

"BIEBER"

Mark has just finished having lunch with a friend and is in a terrific mood. On his way home, he tries out a new option on the Uber app: Destination Trips. Twice a day, drivers can now enter *their* destination, and the app attempts to match the route with riders who are heading in the same general direction. Occasionally it leads to an extra trip or two, helping to offset gas costs, which is particularly beneficial when a driver is forty miles from home but is ready to call it a night.

He enters his home address, and sure enough, a request soon comes in...*Sweet!*

He arrives at the pickup location, and out steps a Justin Bieber look alike. He's wearing yellow-tinted shades, has quaffed hair, is sporting a forearm tattoo, and he has attitude.

But after a year and a half of driving, Mark knows he should never judge a book by its cover, so he pleasantly greets Bieber.

MARK: Hey, how are you doing?
BIEBER: (mumbling) 'Sup?

*Then again, sometimes a book's cover tells the whole story...*But it's only an estimated fifteen-minute trip, so Mark's not sweating the Biebs.

Five minutes into the ride, Bieber mumbles again.

BIEBER: Yo, I need to make a stop along the way.

And just like that, Mark's mood sours. See, Mark knows he's not Bieber's chauffeur. Instead, Uber works the following way: Bieber enters his destination, Mark picks up Bieber, Mark drives Bieber to his destination, Bieber exits the car and says "thank you," Mark says "you're welcome," Mark collects money via the app, and everyone is happy. What Mark *doesn't do* is make stops along the way, only to sit in his car earning eleven cents a minute while missing out on other rides as Bieber does as he pleases.

And it's not as if he is opposed to helping passengers. He's made plenty of concessions in the past. But requests usually include phrases such as "Please," "I'll be quick," "Do you mind?". Mark is cool with that. He understands that things come up, and he's happy to do someone a solid. What he doesn't understand (or tolerate) is *entitlement.* No, entitlement bothers Mark, and within seconds of Bieber's order, he begins to stew.

BIEBER: Yeah, stop right there—at Chipotle.
MARK: Okay, you've got sixty seconds.
BIEBER: What?!
MARK: I'm not your chauffeur. You've got sixty seconds.

With squinted eyes, Bieber looks towards Chipotle, back to Mark, to Chipotle again, and finally settles on Mark.

BIEBER: I'll never be able to order and get my food in a minute.
MARK: Yeah, you're probably right.

Bieber's lips purse.

BIEBER: Yo, man, this why I pay extra for Uber X so you *do* make stops. I'm going here and then I'm going to work.
MARK: Um, no. Uber X just means you're one step above being in a pool. Doesn't mean I'm making stops for you.
BIEBER: But you're getting paid while you wait.
MARK: You know how much we get per minute?—Eleven cents. I'm not going to just sit here while you get lunch for eleven cents a minute.
BIEBER: I've done this before; no one's ever had a problem.
MARK: Good for them.

Perhaps inspired by his badass forearm tattoo, Bieber's voice deepens.

BIEBER: You know, man, if you don't like it, maybe you should find another job.
MARK: Hmmmm? That's interesting. I'm thinking maybe you should find a job that delivers Chipotle.
BIEBER: MAN, I'M JUST TRYING TO MAKE IT TO WORK! IT'S JUST A FEW BLOCKS AWAY!!!
MARK: Cool. And I'm happy to take you to work. Or you can jump out here, get your food, and then walk your burrito eating ass down the street.

In a huff, Bieber exits—his yellow-tinted shades fogging up with each exasperated exhale. Mark swipes the app to close out the trip and drives away.

As he heads home, he knows: A) He could have been nicer to Bieber. B) He's tired of self-entitled millennials thinking they can have their way without being polite, respectful, and courteous.

He weighs A and B for a moment…*I guess "B" won today.*

*Months later, Uber changed its policy by adding an option that allowed riders to input multiple stops. From that point forward, Mark has referred to these rides as a "Bieber".

"Thanks for taking us the few extra blocks. You're the best! 😘"

★★★★★

"UM, HELLO?!"

Two women in their early twenties are patiently waiting to be picked up. Mark pulls up beside them. One immediately gets in the backseat while the other walks around the car to enter the backseat on the driver's side.

Mark greets his first passenger.

MARK: Hi. How are you?

She says nothing.

He's a bit taken back, brushes it off, and greets passenger #2.

MARK: Hi. How are you?

She, too, doesn't respond.

Oooooo-kay.

He pulls away from the curb with steam rising from his forehead... *Damn millennials. What am I?—Their chauffeur?*

He stops at a red light, still ruminating over the lack of common courtesy displayed by younger generations... *No respect. No respect at all...* Suddenly, he notices the car bouncing around a bit. Sensing that the women are moving around energetically, he looks in the rearview mirror to see what they're doing.

What he sees makes his eyes shut tight...*I hate myself...I am a horrible person...I should live in a cave.*

He rolls down the window and gives a homeless man a five-dollar bill.

Ten minutes later, the women exit the car. Mark sends them on their way with an over-exaggerated wave and smile. They, too, wave and smile. They also say goodbye—*in sign language.*

"THE NEW MATH"

Mark's been cheating on Uber—not with Lyft, but by taking on part-time driving duties at the private school where he coaches.

Despite a small student population, there are still plenty of sports teams needing transportation to and from games. A fleet of SUVs sit on campus for that very purpose. With his coaching season now finished, Mark has picked up a few extra driving assignments—and he likes it. The money is better than Uber, he's not using his own gas, there's no wear and tear on his car, and he isn't playing "Rider Roulette"—he pretty much always knows what he's getting into.

Today's passengers are members of the middle school boys' soccer team. With one suburban already full, the remaining five team members are getting settled in his vehicle, and as they do so, Mark is shocked at what he's witnessing... *They're actually talking to one another, and there isn't a cell phone in sight.*

Having now coached at the school for four years, he's become accustomed to an entirely different routine, one which moves like a finely tuned dance: The kids get in the SUV, buckle up, then immediately take out their phones and start scouring their favorite social media sites. On each occasion he's wanted to scream, "Talk to the person next to you! They're literally right there!" To his dismay, the kids have never taken such action on their own... Until today!

As he joyfully turns the ignition key, he notices one boy holding court.

RINGLEADER: Okay, go ahead, guess. If any of you can guess my mom's age I'll give you a piece of gum.

The conversation seems a bit odd, but Mark remembers what he was like in junior high…*I bet she's hot.*

Boys 2-5 start to blurt out their answers.

BOY #2: 41
BOY #3: 44
BOY #4: 36
BOY #5: 28

They all look at Boy #5. Even Mark cocks his head sideways…*28?*

RINGLEADER: Nope. You're all wrong. She's 39.

Boy #1 takes out a piece of gum, waves around the gooey treat as tantalizingly as possible, and then pops it in his mouth.

BOY #2: Wow! Thirty-nine?! So she had you when she was like twenty.

Mark's ears perk up.

BOYS #3-5: That's young!...Wow!…Twenty!!!
RINGLEADER: Yeah, I guess.

Feeling the need to stand up for the great mathematicians over time, Mark decides it's time to butt in.

MARK: You're nineteen?
RINGLEADER: (incredulous) No, I'm thirteen.
MARK: Then how did your mom have you at twenty?

Crickets.

MARK: Think about it. Just take a second and think about it.
RINGLEADER: Shoot, I don't know how old she was!
MARK: Really?! She-is-thir-ty-nine-and-you-are-thir-teen-and-none-of-you-guys-can-fig-ure-out-how-old-she-was-when-she-gave-birth?

He looks in the rearview mirror to find five dumbfounded teenagers staring back at him as if he had just asked them to explain the theory of relativity.

Minutes roll by. No answers.

Finally...

BOY #4: 26!!!

Mark slaps at the steering wheel with pseudo pride.

MARK: Atta boy! I knew you could do it!

Boy #4 puffs his chest while the rest of the crew scramble to try and figure out how he came up with the answer...And so quickly!

With M.I.T. now poised to offer Boy #4 a scholarship, Mark refocuses on the road and shakes his head ...*I weep for the future. Weep, I tell you!*

A few moments pass when suddenly he has a realization: A familiar tone has taken over the SUV. He looks back and sees all five boys have their cell phones out; their chins are tucked to chests, not a word is being said. Yes, habitual silence has won again, having conquered actual human interaction by the simple act of entering a passcode.

And there it is.

"MAKE-UP SEX"

It's a Wednesday afternoon, and rush hour traffic is in full affect. Mark is halfway to LAX after picking up a couple by The Grove. There's no surge on the trip which is making the trek feel much more painful. He's also noticed that his knee is acting up from constantly shifting his foot from the gas pedal to the brake and back again. *Painful!* His back is tightening up. *Painful!* No auditions in weeks. *Painful!* But what's most painful?—The couple in the backseat...

Mark is loading a husband and wife's giant suitcases into the trunk of his car. His spine feels as if it's about to snap in half.

HUSBAND: Hey, thanks, but be careful. There are some valuable items in there.

Mark looks over with disapproving eyes.

HUSBAND: Right. Sorry. Let me help you.

Just as they are barely squeezing in the luggage, the wife zips out of their condo and makes her presence known.

WIFE: We're running late; please get us to the airport as fast as you can.

Mark rolls his eyes...*Here we go.*

During his time as a driver, he's had his share of passengers running late for flights. He's been yelled at for not being in the carpool lane; he's been yelled at for *being* in the carpool lane. One person wants Waze navigation, the next wants Google Maps.

Each time he's wanted to say, "This is not on me! If you're late, it's on you!" But, instead, he always sticks to a pat answer.

MARK: I will get you there as quickly as I can while still being safe.
WIFE: Yes, of course. What app are you using?

Eye roll

MARK: Waze.
WIFE: Yeah. Okay. Good.

I'm so glad you approve.

He gets in the car, already knowing this is going to be an arduous trip. Within minutes, his premonition proves correct: The couple begin to bicker non-stop. His only option is to sit back and listen to them repeatedly berate one another.

The husband appears to be fifteen years older than she and comes across as more worldly—at least in his mind. He's conniving and knows how to push her buttons. Meanwhile, she is passive-aggressive and tries to shut him down with—in her mind—logic, which he then flips right back around, and they're at it again.

To make matters worse, they work in the same industry and have high end clients.

WIFE: Well, I guess that's the last time I hear from Beyonce!
HUSBAND: You know you fucked me on that last deal for $27,000, right?!
WIFE: You don't know what you're doing!!
HUSBAND: I've been at this before you were born!!
WIFE: *Bark! Bark! Bark!*
HUSBAND: *Woof! Woof! Woof!*

It doesn't stop.

With the trip now twenty-five minutes deep, Mark not only has a headache, but he's also bitter. He's bitter with them, he's bitter with life, he's bitter knowing the bombastic buffoons in the backseat will most likely be having great make-up sex later while the best he will have is popcorn, a tequila concoction, and Netflix…*Oh, wait. That's right: I don't have Netflix. I can't even afford Netflix!!!*

After another back and forth screaming fit, the wife gets on her phone. Mark isn't sure if she's truly making a call or just needs a break, and he doesn't care.

With his wife out of the equation, the husband shifts his attention.

HUSBAND: So, Mark, do you enjoy driving for Uber?
MARK: Not today.

The husband takes this in, and the battle is on…

Ding, ding. Mark has come out of the corner swinging. Husband dances around the ring

HUSBAND: I'm sorry. Are we putting you in a bad mood?
MARK: Nah, man, it's cool.

Mark pushes husband into the ropes. Husband tries to bob and weave

HUSBAND: We're not usually like this. We never fight.
MARK: Whatever you say, man.

Mark lands a stiff jab. Husband rolls out of the corner

HUSBAND: Um, so how long have you driven for Uber?
MARK: Too long.

Oooo, Mark lands a right cross! Husband staggers, but stays on his feet

HUSBAND: Is this your full-time job?
MARK: No. I would have jumped off a bridge by now.

There's a clean left hook by Mark! It buckles husband, but he's undeterred! What a will, what an ego!

HUSBAND: What else do you do?
MARK: I'm an actor.
HUSBAND: Oh. How's that going?
MARK: Well, I'm still driving people to LAX during rush hour, so what does that tell you?

Oh my! Mark lands a jaw-breaking uppercut! Down goes husband! Down goes husband!

Yes, that did it. The knockout punch has been delivered, and their conversation comes to an abrupt halt. Which—as it turns out—is fine and dandy with the husband, because ol' wife-y has just ended her call and they're at it again.

The following twenty minutes are no better: They argue about the convention they are going to, they argue about dinner reservations, they argue about who *is* and who *is not* coming to dinner; but, mostly, they argue about their flight which they—despite Mark's best efforts—are *NOT* going to catch because of the high end items they are carrying, which needed to be checked-in an hour before the flight's departure.

WIFE: I can't believe we're going to miss the flight!!!!
HUSBAND: I can't believe you made us miss the flight!!!
MARK: I can't believe this is my life.

They arrive at LAX. Mark starts unloading their luggage.

HUSBAND: Thanks. Sorry about the arguing. We truly aren't normally like this.

Mark continues to unload and does not look back.

MARK: Cool.
HUSBAND: I feel a big role coming your way. I'm a lucky guy, I know these things.
MARK: Cool.

The husband begins saying something else, but Mark has already slammed the trunk, closed his door, and pulled away.

A moment later, the app chimes. He pulls over, pops the trunk, and gets out of his car. A young couple approach.

HUSBAND: Mark?

He eyes them.

MARK: Tell me something: Are you guys getting along?
HUSBAND: What?
MARK: Are you getting along? Like are you in the middle of an argument, you're mad at each other, you're both having bad days? Ya know, *"Getting along?"*

They look at one another.

COUPLE: No, we're good.
MARK: Okay, I'll give you a ride. Get in.

He loads their bags, starts the trip, and begins fantasizing about tequila, popcorn, and Netfl—...ESPN...that surely await him later that evening.

"He was a fantastic driver. Nice guy, great conversation. An enjoyable non-stressful ride to the airport."

"HOLD ON TIGHT"

Mark circles a cul-de-sac in Valley Village and comes to a stop. He looks over and sees his passenger, *Kyle,* sitting on the front steps of an adjacent apartment building. Kyle's head is bowed, but eventually he looks up, sees Mark, and begrudgingly gets to his feet. It's a Tuesday morning after a three-day weekend, and Kyle looks like he's been drinking the whole seventy-two hours.

He gets in the backseat.

KYLE: Hey, how you doin', Mark?
MARK: Okay, Kyle. How are you doing?
KYLE: Ah, I'm all right.

Mark swipes the app and sees the destination is close to where he grew up.

About a block into the trip, he attempts to start a conversation—Kyle looks like he's got some stories to tell.

MARK: How was your holiday weekend?

There's a brief pause.

KYLE: To be honest, it was horrible.

MARK: Oh. Sorry to hear that.
KYLE: Thanks.

While Kyle's voice reeks of someone who is tired and upset, Mark isn't sensing any bitterness; he comes across as a nice guy...*Don't say anything more; just leave him be.*

Neither says a word for the next dozen minutes, but as they cross the 405 freeway and pass by Mark's old stomping grounds, he tries breaking the ice once more.

MARK: You from around here?
KYLE: Yeah. You?
MARK: Yep. Right over there. You could probably throw a rock and hit the house I grew up in—assuming, of course, that you've got a really good arm.

Kyle releases a tiny laugh, but his mind still seems to be someplace else.

KYLE: Hey, look, Mark, I apologize for not being friendlier.
MARK: No, no, it's all good. People often don't want to talk.
KYLE: It's just...My dad died on Sunday.

Instantaneously, Mark feels sickened, but he quickly speaks up.

MARK: I'm so sorry, Kyle. You seem like a great guy. I'm sure your dad was very proud of you.
KYLE: Thanks. It's just really hard.
MARK: I get it; my dad passed a few years ago.
KYLE: Oh, sorry...This is so tough. My mom is already gone, so I don't have either of them now. Is your mom still around?

MARK: Yeah, she is.
KYLE: Do yourself a favor: Hold on tight to her whenever you can. You just never know.

Mark takes this in. It's been a struggle with his mom's health lately. Twice over the previous week she had to go to the ER; she's also beginning to have extensive back problems. The fact that she looks older and weaker every time he sees her, only adds to his concerns.

Kyle's voice breaks him from his thoughts.

KYLE: My dad was a great guy, not just as a father but also as a friend.
MARK: I feel ya.

For the next few minutes, Kyle tells Mark about his dad, the relationship they had, and how good of a person he was. Kyle's tone, despite his loss and the pain he's going through, remains positive throughout...*Seems like a cool guy. Man, I hate watching people go through this.*

They soon reach his destination. Mark puts out his hand; Kyle shakes it as if they have been friends for life.

MARK: Really sorry for your loss, Kyle.
KYLE: Thanks. Take care.
MARK: You too.

The moment the door shuts, Mark reaches forward, turns off the app, and makes a call.

VOICE: Hello?

MARK: Hey, Mom. I was just thinking about you. I thought maybe we could grab some lunch together.
MOM: Oh, I'd love that.
MARK: Me too. I'll be by soon.

"HOME, SWEET HOME"

MARCH 7, 2017

Mark exits his car in the Mid-Wilshire area. He looks at his reflection in the side window, fixes a loose strand of hair, takes in a deep breath, and confidently strides forward…

* * *

It's been a slow last month and a half since he worked on *Speechless*. He's only had one commercial audition and none for TV or movies. Pilot Season is rushing by, and his career feels like it's coming to a grinding halt. His quest to find a new manager has been equally fruitless. Unsolicited submissions and referrals from entertainment industry friends have only led to one meeting: a husband and wife team whom he immediately knows is not the right fit.

As he leaves that meeting, wondering how wise it was to have left his former reps, another idea comes to mind.

He calls his friend Maria.

MARIA: Mr. Bloom, what's shakin'?
MARK: Not much, unfortunately. I'm kind of hoping you might be able to help me out in that department.
MARIA: Sure. What can I do for ya?

MARK: Well, as you know, I've been trying to find a new management team, and I thought about you. You like your managers, right?
MARIA: Love them. They're like family.
MARK: That sounds good. Do you think you could get me a meeting?
MARIA: I definitely think they'd be happy to meet with "Mr. I was on eight shows last year." Just one thing.
MARK: What's that?
MARIA: You can't be "Grumpy Mark." You have to be "Happy Mark."
MARK: Yeah, of course.
MARIA: Well, I recommended someone one time, and my managers told me she was boring and negative. They don't want to meet people who are jaded and not excited about being actors.
MARK: I promise I won't be boring or negative, and I'll put on my best "I'm excited to be an actor" face.
MARIA: That's what I like to hear. I'm actually seeing them this afternoon. I'll let them know that I have a fabulous actor friend who needs a new manager.
MARK: You always say the nicest things.
MARIA: Well, not always. But for you, Bloom, I'm happy to do what I can do.
MARK: Thanks, Maria.

Later in the day, he researches the company. They only represent forty actors, which is in stark contrast to the three hundred his former managers had on their roster...*Nice*...The situation seems ideal. Now he just has to wow them, and hopefully they wow him back.

...A fanned-out pile of entertainment magazines lay on a coffee table that sits between Mark and his prospective new reps: Hank and Lily. Hank is fun and gregarious but serious when he needs to be. Lily is a little more reserved but is nice and professional. They have asked their assistant, Nina, to hold all calls, and Mark is already liking the vibe.

The meeting lasts for an hour and a half. Discussions range from the present climate of the entertainment industry, to what Mark is looking for in a manager, to what Hank and Lily feel they can offer if they were to work together. There are plenty of laughs, plenty of getting down to the nuts and bolts of what their relationship would look like, plenty of time for Mark to express how he sees his career moving forward.

No aspect of the meeting causes him to have concern. He feels in tune with Hank and Lily, and Nina too. They're energetic, professional, fun, and already feel like family just as Maria had said.

LILY: It was great meeting you. We just need to discuss things. We'll give you a call tomorrow.
MARK: Sounds good. Talk to you then.

He exits the building just as he had entered—with strides powered by confidence.

The next day, Lily calls.

MARK: Hi. How are you?
LILY: I'm good. So, Hank and I talked it over and—
MARK: *...And??*
LILY: —And we'd be thrilled to represent you if you're interested.

Mark performs a horrible moonwalk across his living room floor.

MARK: Absolutely! Can't wait to get started.
LILY: Great. We'll have Nina send over some info to get you all squared away, and we'll get things going.
MARK: Awesome! Thanks so much. I really look forward to working with you and Hank.
LILY: We look forward to it as well…Oh, wait, Hank wants to say something. I'm holding up the phone.
HANK: (from seemingly across the office) Congratulations, "Bloomin' Onion!" Welcome to the party!

Mark laughs…*Apparently, I already have a new nickname.*

More importantly, he has a full team of reps again, and he's confident they'll do everything in their power to take him to the next level.

* * *

Two nights later, his episode of *Speechless* airs. The following morning, his phone rings at 10 AM.

MARK: Hello?
VOICE: Hey, Mark, it's Lily.
MARK: Oh, hey, Lily. Sorry, I didn't recognize the phone number.
LILY: That's because I'm on my way into the office, so I'm on my cell.
MARK: Oh, okay. What's up?
LILY: Well, I watched your episode of *Speechless* last night. I want to get your thoughts on how it came out.

Mark pulls the phone away from his ear and looks at it quizzically. Not once has he gotten a call like this before…*This is amazing! Thank you, thank you, thank you, Maria.*

MARK: Well, I was pretty happy with it. There was this one part where…

They talk for the next fifteen minutes. Mark has found his new home, and he couldn't be happier.

"JUST DO IT"

It's mid-afternoon, mid-week, in the Mid-Valley. A request comes in from *Tony* at—wouldn't you know it—Mark's alma mater, Birmingham High School.

As he drives down the same side-street he had travelled years earlier—chuckling the whole way—a flood of memories flow into his mind: some good, some bad, some reflective. He feels transported to thirty-two years earlier as if he had never left.

There are a few changes, however. An extra gate has been erected since the last time he was on campus, and the mural gifted by his graduating class has been painted over. This happened when the school's mascot was changed from "Braves" to "Patriots" for politically correct reasons. He understands the thought process behind the change, but in his heart, he'll always be a *Birmingham Brave.*

Tony opens the passenger door.

TONY: Is it okay to sit in the front seat?
MARK: Absolutely. How was school?
TONY: Good. How's your day going?
MARK: Not bad. Although I'm trippin' a little right now.
TONY: Why's that?

MARK: Because a long time ago—and I mean a long time ago—I went to this very high school.

A huge smile rises on Tony's face.

TONY: No way!! Really?!
MARK: Yep.
TONY: Wow. How long ago?
MARK: Over thirty years. I graduated in 1985.
TONY: Wow. That *is* a long time ago.

Mark looks over.

MARK: Well, you didn't have to put it like that.
TONY: (laughing) Sorry.
MARK: No problem. But you're right: it *was* a long time ago.
TONY: What was it like back then?
MARK: "What was it like back then?" Dang, Tony, it's not like we had dinosaurs walking on campus.

Tony laughs but genuinely seems intrigued.

MARK: It was a good school. One of the best parts was how much diversity we had. Every nationality was represented: white, black, Asian, Hispanic, Middle Eastern. Everyone seemed to get along really well. I remember maybe two fights in the three years I was there. It was good.

He takes a moment to realize how fortunate he was, knowing not all kids have the same experience.

MARK: What about you? You like it?

TONY: Yeah, it's fine. I'm just finishing my junior year, got some midterms right now, then finals, senior year, and it's off to college.

Mark's getting a good vibe from Tony: he's nice, well spoken, and appears to be on his way to a bright future. However, despite Tony's positive attributes, Mark still shifts into "Old-Man Talk" mode.

MARK: Well, all that is good, and college will be one of the best experiences of your life, but enjoy your senior year of high school. If I could go back in time, I definitely would have done things differently.
TONY: Really? What would you have done?

He takes a moment to think it over.

MARK: Well, mostly I would have been more social. I wish I had met more people and got involved in school activities, especially during my senior year.
TONY: Hmmmmm?
MARK: And the beautiful thing about being a senior is once you get past first semester, and all your college applications are in, it's easy sailing.
TONY: I'll definitely remember that. Did you go to college?
MARK: Yep. UC Santa Barbara.
TONY: Oh, wow. That's one of my choices.
MARK: Nice. I definitely enjoyed my time there. Although, admittedly, the admissions were a lot easier back then. I don't envy your generation and how hard it is to get into college. But you seem like a hard-working kid, so I think you'll make it if that's where you want to go.

Tony nods.

MARK: So, are you involved in any sports or other activities?
TONY: I played soccer, and I was thinking about playing baseball next year, but I don't think I'm going to.
MARK: Why?
TONY: I don't know. I've got a lot of friends on the team, and I was good when I was younger, but…I don't know.

They stop at a red light.

MARK: Okay, Tony, you listen to me right now: You're trying out for the team next year. No excuses. You have a bunch of friends on the team?
TONY: Yeah, a lot of friends. A lot of good players too. I haven't played competitively in years.
MARK: That's okay, don't worry about that. Look, here's the thing: It doesn't matter if you end up being a stud player or don't get off the bench the whole season. You've got almost a full year to get your baseball skills back and you'll make the team, and *that's* what's most important. It's all about the experience: the camaraderie that goes with sports, the competition, and getting to be with your buddies all the way through it. I'm still really tight with guys I played basketball with. In fact, I'm even close with my coaches.
TONY: Really?
MARK: Yep, I see them all the time. Listen, you can't get these years back. Enjoy being with your friends. Don't you dare not go out for that team next year.

Tony processes Mark's advice and keeps nodding.

TONY: Hey, do you have any kids?
MARK: Nah. It never worked out. I always wanted to be a dad, but it just didn't happen.
TONY: It still could.

MARK: Yeah, maybe. I'm really just waiting for my next life.

Tony chuckles.

MARK: But I've gotten the chance to coach basketball—although this might be my final year—and I taught karate for a long time, so at least I feel like I've influenced some kids…Hopefully, positively.

Tony laughs again; Mark smiles at his response.

TONY: Ya know—and I hope you don't mind me saying this—I think you'd make a great dad.

!!!

Mark is taken aback. The words sit in the air for a moment before he can speak again.

MARK: Oh…Wow. Thank you, Tony. That's about the nicest thing anyone's ever said to me.

Tony shrugs.

TONY: You just seem to have a lot of good advice. I hope you keep coaching at least.
MARK: Yeah, we'll see.

They arrive at Tony's destination a moment later.

MARK: Well, it was good meeting you, young man. Good luck with your midterms, enjoy summer, and what else are you going to do?—

TONY: —Play baseball next year. I'm going to. Thanks.

Tony exits, and Mark begins to drive away. But within a block, he pulls over, draws in a deep breath, and wipes his eyes.

Damn onions. Damn, damn onions.

"Thanks!"

★★★★★

"WHY DO I CHASE THE CAT?"

Mark pulls up to a street corner in Inglewood to pick up *Lionel.*

Seconds later, a man in his late 60s to early 70s makes his way into the back seat and makes an announcement.

LIONEL: Well, I don't have cancer yet.

Mark has been on the road for a few hours and has hit that point in the day where words just fly over his head, but Lionel's proclamation has the synapses in his brain firing once again.

MARK: Oh? Did you just have a doctor's appointment?
LIONEL: Yep. No cancer.
MARK: Well, good. Why did you think you had cancer?
LIONEL: My PSA numbers were high. The doctors had given me some antibiotics to see if that would help.
MARK: Did your numbers go down?
LIONEL: Yeah, a little. I've had biopsies before. Never been an issue. We'll see.
MARK: Well, good luck.
LIONEL: Thanks.

Lionel looks around the car.

LIONEL: You drive full time?
MARK: No. This is job number four. What about yourself? You retired?
LIONEL: Nope. I work as a probations officer.
MARK: Wow. You must have seen a thing or two. How is that as a job?
LIONEL: I hate it. It's just a bunch of people who really aren't trying to be helpful. It's a bad system. No one cares.

Mark eyebrows lift; he finds himself quite intrigued by Lionel—although he's not exactly sure why. Maybe it's the easy-going manner in which Lionel speaks, or maybe he just wants some quality conversation for a change, but he's definitely intrigued by his forthright companion.

MARK: Where are you from, Lionel?
LIONEL: Minnesota. Grew up there; went to school there.
MARK: What school?
LIONEL: University of Minnesota.
MARK: The Golden Gophers!

Lionel perks up.

LIONEL: You know them?
MARK: I'm a big college basketball fan.
LIONEL: That's funny; they're usually horrible.
MARK: Yeah, but a while ago they had a run or two.
LIONEL: True…A long while ago.
MARK: How long have you been in Los Angeles?
LIONEL: Twenty-eight years.
MARK: Oh, okay. That's more than a minute. You must like it.

LIONEL: Hate it. Everything's so expensive. And this traffic!

He motions towards the cars surrounding them. Mark laughs. He finds Lionel's candidness to be appealing if for no other reason than Los Angeles is often short on truth and long on deception.

MARK: Well, shoot, sir, we need to find you something that you like.

Lionel releases a tiny laugh and looks out the side window. He appears to be searching for a long-lost pleasure, maybe something he took for granted as a young man but now appreciates.

LIONEL: You know what I still like?

Mark glances in the rearview mirror, highly anticipating Lionel's next frank comment.

LIONEL: Seeing beautiful women.

A smile grows on Mark's face. He knows the comment was not said in a creepy manner. There's just something about a vibrant, beautiful woman that can spark *any* man at *any* age.

MARK: Never gets old, does it?
LIONEL: Nope.

Lionel snaps out of his daydream and leans forward.

LIONEL: But with my prostate and all, I'm like a toothless dog chasing a cat: even if I caught one, what the heck am I going to do anyway?

The two break into uproarious laughter as they pull up to Lionel's house.

LIONEL: You take care, Mark.
MARK: Yeah, you do the same, Lionel. You do the same.

"DARLING NIKKI...WELL, MAYBE NOT"

It's a Friday night. Mark has just dropped off a couple on Ventura Boulevard when a request comes in to pick up *Nikki... Nikki, huh?*

His mind immediately trails off to the sexy Prince song, "Darling Nikki." A few salacious fantasies dance around his skull, but they're quickly brushed aside because there's one thing Mark knows for certain: Nikki will *not* be a stunning, sexy woman.

During his time as an Uber driver he has noticed an odd phenomenon: The sexier a woman's name sounds the less likely she will be and vice versa. In the Uber universe, Nikkis, Crystals, and Ambers can never hold a candle to Claires, Ruths, and Gertrudes. It's uncanny.

As he makes a U-Turn, he giggles in anticipation... *All right, Nikki, let's see what you're all about.*

And sure enough, she has taken his theory to a whole other level because *she* is a *he*. Not that Nikki is transgender or a crossdresser, instead, he's like Nikki Sixx. Not that he looks like Nikki Sixx, just that he's named Nikki and he's a guy. This Nikki looks more like a smaller version of Alexander Godunov's character, "Karl," in the movie *Die Hard*: He has long dirty blonde hair and strong facial features. Plus, when he says hello, and Mark hears a Scandinavian accent, the moniker seems much more appropriate...*I'm just going to think of him as "Karl" because "Nikki" still seems like there should be a gorgeous, sexy woman in the backseat and that's certainly not the case.*

The app is swiped and they're off.

After some friendly banter to start the trip, both go silent, which suits Mark just fine. Unfortunately, a few moments later, Karl has other ideas: he begins blaring music from his phone. While it's not uncommon for passengers to play music, they usually wear headphones, which helps muffle the sound. But Karl?—Oh, Karl is not shy. He is *blasting* his music. House music at that! He gives no warning. No, "Hey, do you mind if I…?". Just blasting.

Mark wriggles in his seat… *Why can't people be considerate?!… This is a shared space, Karl!!*

To make matters worse, Karl keeps rewinding to one particular spot then plays the same fifteen second stanza over and over: heavy base, synchronized sounds, screeching four-word lyrics—"*Yeah, I wannnnnnt you!… Yeah, I want you!* (boom-boom-ba-boom-boom-boom) *Yeah, I waaannnnnnt you!*"—Stop. Rewind. And it starts all over. "*Yeahhhhhhhh, I wannnnnnt you!*"

Mark looks at the app. There's still twenty-five minutes to go. He tries to relax by taking in a few deep breaths… It's not helping.

"*Yeaaaaaahhhhhh, I waaaannnnnnntttt youuuuuuuuuuu!*"

Finally, the "music" ceases.

Thank you.

The quiet tranquility is only temporary, however, as soon Karl begins playing another track from his hellish playlist. It's the same routine: heavy base, synchronized beats, four-word nothingness, annnndddddd repeat.

Now Mark's pissed. He transforms himself into Bruce Willis' *Die Hard* character, "John McClane."

I'm going to give you one star, Karl! Yippee Kai Yay, Motherfucker! Yippee Kai-Mother-Fuckin-Yay!

KARL: Hey, do you have an auxiliary cor—?
MARK: NOPE!!

Karl sinks in his seat, he hits pause.

Silence.
Amazing Silence.
Fantabulous Silence.
Karl—

KARL: Do you ever have people working in your car when you drive them around?

Mark peeks in the rearview mirror. He doesn't want to engage, but he knows he can't ignore the question.

MARK: Sure, but it's usually on a laptop. Not like this. Let me guess: You're a music producer?
KARL: Yes.
MARK: Mmmm hmmmm.

They revert to quietness, pleasing Mark to no end...*Yippee Kai Yay, Karl! One Star!*

KARL: So, what kind of music do you like?

Mark bites down on his bottom lip...*Oh, don't you start getting all nice with me! I'm bitter and angry! I want to relish in my John McClane transformation! You are the enemy, Karl! One star for you! Yippee Kai Yay!!!*

MARK: Well, I grew up on stuff like Michael Jackson and classic rock. And back in the day, I even liked house music like you were just playing. But my all-time favorite band is *Earth, Wind, and Fire.*
KARL: Oh, I love *Earth, Wind, and Fire.*

Damn it, Karl! Stop being friendly! We only have a handful of minutes left. I want to rejoice in the misery that is my life!

KARL: I particularly like "September." How about you?
MARK: Well, I tend to appreciate many of their songs that weren't so mainstream.
KARL: So, you don't like "September?"

Mark laughs...*Gosh darn it, Karl! Laughter is a sure sign of enjoyment! Let me bathe in my self-loathing!*

MARK: No, I like "September." All their stuff is great.
KARL: True.

For the last few minutes of the ride they talk about music, Karl's home country—Sweden—and his favorite dessert... cupcakes.

They pull up to his destination.

KARL: Thank you so much for the ride, Mark…I appreciate you.

And there it is: The ultimate friendly dagger. Mark smiles and shuts his eyes in defeat.

MARK: You're welcome, Kar—I mean Nikki.

The door closes and Mark surrenders to the warm, fuzzy feelings that now inhabit his body. He smiles and reaches for the app.

Yippee kai yay, Nikki. Emphasis on the "Yippee" and the "Yay."… 5 stars.

"Great driver, good conversation. Perfect gentleman-5 stars!"

"THE TRUE CHAMP"

APRIL 11, 2017

Mark looks up at the faces staring down at him…Something doesn't seem right…

* * *

Part of the beauty of turning fifty is that many of Mark's friends are also turning fifty, which means celebrations and get-togethers with close friends and friends from the distant past are filling up his calendar.

Per usual, however, he's worried about money. At the beginning of the year he planned out two weekend getaways for March, but now that the excursions are right around the corner, he's anxious. Even a simple weekend escape is considered a huge vacation to him, and his bank account doesn't justify such travel. To counter his financial woes, he's been driving more often than usual to build a getaway fund, knowing that when he's gone, not only will he be spending more than usual, but he also won't be driving.

But one evening he decides to take a break so he can watch *The Academy Awards*. While he's realistic and doesn't have any grand visions of ever winning an *Oscar*, he finds the ceremony and speeches to be inspiring. Plus, dreaming about what his speech *would* be like is a nice mental diversion from reality.

As the broadcast takes a commercial break, he closes his eyes...*I'd like to thank my mom and dad, my family, and all my great friends who've been so supportive over the years*...A smile arcs across his face.

He continues dreaming away when suddenly his phone starts to *buzz!-hum!*-and *ding!* as it never has before.

He opens his eyes and sees three texts.

—"You made it! You made it on the Academy Awards!"
—"Congratulations, dude! I knew you'd make it on the AA's someday! LOL!"
—"Hey, I saw you! So exciting! Congratulations!"

Surprisingly, the last text is from Daniella, but he still can't figure out what in the world everyone is talking about. While he takes pride in his daydreaming abilities—if there is such a thing—he doesn't remotely believe his talents are powerful enough to transport him to the *actual* Academy Awards. Last he checked he's still sitting on his couch, and the only thing in his apartment resembling a golden trophy is the bottle of Patron sitting in the freezer.

He responds to Daniella.

MARK: What's going on? My phone just blew up.
DANIELLA: Your Geico commercial! It just showed during the *Oscars!*
MARK: It did! I'm literally sitting here watching, but I looked away for a second!

He logs onto Facebook. Friends are posting similar messages. His favorite is from his longtime buddy, Dave: "My boy, Mudge, finally made it on the *Academy Awards!* Congrats, Big Daddy!"

He sits back, elation running through his veins...*Now that the commercial is officially running, I can truly enjoy my getaways.*

The first Friday of March, he drives up the coast to his alma mater, U.C. Santa Barbara, to meet up with his four roommates from sophomore year. It's been thirty years since "SKEBS"—an acronym of their last names, which they later admitted sounded like an STD—shared a three-bedroom apartment in the legendary college town of Isla Vista.

As is often the case with old friends, they have gone their own ways over the years: different professions, different lives, different views of the world. There's been marriages and divorces, lots of kids, some successes and some failures. But as the five assemble at a Spanish style hotel in downtown Santa Barbara, it's as if time hasn't passed—They're right back to being nineteen and twenty-year-olds. Quickly they fall back into the rhythms of their friendships. Heartfelt hugs are exchanged, stories are relived, and inside jokes make them laugh for minutes on end. There is a bond between them that will last forever.

Their time together leads to one of the best weekends Mark's ever had. They revisit campus, marveling at old buildings that still stand and new ones that have been erected. At every turn, at least one of them has a story to tell. They eat at old haunts and wolf down a whole mess of food that seemed a lot easier to digest when they were college students.

On Saturday, they walk through the streets of Isla Vista and head to the apartment they had shared. It's a beautiful day, and college kids are out in abundance. It all seems like yesterday, yet so far away.

As they excitedly make their way down the street—their apartment just coming into view—they notice a group of five male students walking towards them. As the groups pass, SKEBS can't help but stare: It's as if they are viewing themselves from thirty years earlier.

MARK: Guys! That was us!

The college group has heard the chatter and spin to them.

MARK: Live it up, boys, because I hate to tell you this: in thirty years, you're going to look like us!

SKEBS bursts out laughing, sloppily high-five one another, and continue their way down the street.

Unfortunately, when they arrive at their old place, "Casa Del Sur," no one is home, leaving them somewhat disappointed. But they take pictures on the staircase leading up to the apartment and tell every student walking by how they had lived there thirty years earlier. Some don't care and brush them off, others are intrigued, knowing that someday they'll be in similar shoes.

The group revisits more spots throughout the day, have a great dinner a little later, and then say their goodbyes the next morning.

As Mark drives south on the 101 Freeway, the shimmering Pacific Ocean on his right, he beams as he recounts all the memories that have risen...*I wonder if we'll ever get together again?*

The question gives him pause. A feeling of melancholy builds deep within him...*If it's meant to happen, it will happen. But I'll always love you SKEBS.*

Two weeks later, he's off to San Francisco for the 50th birthday of one of his oldest buddies, Dan. The memories differ from the SKEBS reunion but are just as profound. Unlike SKEBS, Dan, Mark, and many of their friends, see and talk to one another frequently. They've all known each other since they were little kids. Their stories run long and deep.

There are also a few friendships rekindled over the weekend, guys that Mark has only seen a handful of times since high school.

At the big party on Saturday night, he is talking with two such friends: Donnie and Malik. They played basketball together back in the day, and as buried stories get dug up, he informs them that he recently started to play ball again. His excitement is quickly halted.

DONNIE: Don't do it, Bloom.
MARK: What?
MALIK: Yeah, don't do it. Everyone we know who plays after forty-five gets hurt.
DONNIE: Ankle, knee, hip, something.

Mark shakes his head at the notion. He's always kept himself in good shape and is still very limber from all of his years practicing karate.

MARK: I'll be all right.
MALIK: Okay, you've always been a little different from everyone else, Bloom. But don't say we didn't warn you.

They all laugh then it's on to relive another memory.

The weekend consists of non-stop laughs, drinks, and stories. On Sunday, a smaller group gathers for brunch as a final send off.

It's the perfect capper to the weekend, but as the last plate is cleared from the table, and the merriment dies down, out of nowhere, Dan's stepfather, Barry, stands up.

BARRY: Hey, Mudge! You're a celebrity!! Look!

Everyone turns to see the Geico commercial playing on a nearby television. When it concludes, exaggerated applause fills the room.

MARK: Nothing like your friends busting your balls. Thanks, guys.

Later that night he arrives back in L.A., feeling pretty great about life. In fact, there's only one problem: auditions have been scarce lately. He knows his managers are still determining how to market him, but he also knows in another month the town will slow down to a crawl as the "Summer Slowdown" kicks in.

Frustrated and needing to clear his mind, he decides to go for a hike one morning. As he's about to head into the hills, his phone buzzes. It's his manager, Hank... *Thank goodness, an audition.*

HANK: Bloomin' Onion, whatcha doin'?
MARK: Hey, Hank, just about to start a hike. What's happening?
HANK: Do you have a minute before you go?
MARK: Yeah, sure. What's up?
HANK: Well, Lily and I were talking. We think you need to get some new headshots.

He instantly becomes sick to his stomach...*Are you kidding me?!*

If there's one phrase an actor can't stand hearing from their reps it's "You need new headshots." The request always comes across as a big red flag: The reps can't get the actor out for auditions, so it must be the headshots. But Mark has been around the block too many times to know that this frequently isn't the case. Headshots, like all aspects of acting, are subjective. Show ten agents, managers, and casting directors the same photo, and you'll get ten different opinions.

The suggestion literally deflates him; he releases a very audible sigh.

Hearing this, Hank shifts to serious mode.

HANK: Whoa, whoa, whoa; just hear me out for a second. This is what's going on: I've been getting on the phone and pitching you to casting directors. They're looking at your profile, and even though *I know* you're perfect for the role, they don't see it in your pics.

Mark takes a step back...*He's getting busy casting directors to look at my profile? This is sounding better.*

HANK: So, here's what I'm thinking: Right now your shots are too commercial. They're not way over the top like some actor's pictures who are wearing doctor's scrubs as if to say, "Look at me, I'm a doctor." Your pictures are nothing like that. But when I think of you, I think quirky dad, sarcastic guy, hard-ass "go fuck yourself" lawyer. Is that fair?
MARK: Yeah, I'll go with that.
HANK: Good. So, your present shots are a little over the top in that regard. They say, "Hey, look at me! I can play those roles. See? Look at my little smirk. I'm a smartass." I don't want that.

Shots like that are only good for getting co-star roles. They're not good for guest-star roles and recurring roles and being a series regular. I want your pictures to be so subtle—so your complete essence—that when casting sees them they're like, "That guy's interesting. I want to meet him." They don't even know why. They just know there's something there. That's what I want for you. Does that make sense?

He is blown away. Hank's words are a dream come true. He's now 100% certain he's with the right team: they're cool, they're fighting for him, and they want to take him to the next level.

MARK: That sounds great.
HANK: And look, if you want to take some pics of yourself first, that's fine; we understand that new headshots are expensive. So, try it yourself, save some money, and if those don't work we've got a list of photographers we really like, and we can go from there.
MARK: That's amazing. Thank you so much.

With Mark's assurance, Hank immediately falls back to his silly side.

HANK: You're welcome, Bloomin' Onion! Now go enjoy that hike and we'll talk soon!

As they hang up, Mark feels as if he's planting his feet in the starting blocks of a career changing moment.

Over the next couple of days, he buys a remote trigger, sets up a tripod, and takes pictures of himself. Unfortunately, Hank and Lily don't find the shots to be quite right. It's disappointing, but he understands...*Maybe it would be better to just spend the money and hire one of the photographers on their list*...But as he drives around all afternoon and is reminded just how tough money is to come by, he decides he'll try one last time to get that perfect headshot.

The following morning, he heads to the gym to get in a little workout before taking the pictures. After a quick warmup, he makes his way to the basketball court to play some two-on-two. Midway through the second game, he has the ball at the top of the key. He fakes right, takes one big step with his left, and heads towards the basket. As he does so, a fellow player steps on the back of his leg, sending him to the ground. As he turns to see who had stepped on him, he discovers that no one is there.

He looks up at the faces staring down at him…Something doesn't seem right…

* * *

Three days later, he has reconstructive surgery on his ruptured right Achilles tendon.

The injury is devastating on many levels…*How am I going to get around? What am I going to do for money? I can't even drive since it's my right foot. And acting? Dammit! I won't be able to audition for months. Whatever momentum I had will be completely washed away. Shit!*

The next few months are difficult. Days are spent reading, browsing the Internet, and taking naps. At night, he watches Netflix—which he's finally ordered—and sits quietly by himself. He appreciates his many friends who take him to the market and to doctor's appointments; the occasional drop-by visit is heavenly. There's only one person he has trouble seeing: his mom. He feels helpless when she comes over, like a little kid again. After her first couple of visits, he pushes any future ones aside by telling her that he's okay and would prefer to just be alone.

Fortunately, the injury heals relatively quickly.

DOCTOR: You're the second-best patient I've ever had.
MARK: Second?
DOCTOR: Yeah, there was this stuntman I operated on who was doing backflips after three months.
MARK: Hmmm? Well, in all honesty, I'm perfectly fine with the silver medal and getting back to my life.

After 2 1/2 months of multiple casts and a boot, he begins rehab and is ready to get back to his normal routine. Health is no longer taken for granted; the simple act of walking around the neighborhood is exhilarating. Plus, episodic season is right around the corner, and he has some catching up to do if the year will be a success.

The day after taking of the boot for good, he wakes up, slowly makes his way to the bathroom, and steps in front of the mirror. He's a little afraid to view himself. There's been one thought that's been running through his mind for weeks. He lifts his eyes and focuses on his reflection, and when he does, the same thought comes to the forefront of his consciousness. He sees the wrinkles etching deeper into his face, the brown hairs turning gray on top of his head, and he can't help but to let out a tiny laugh at the decision he's made...*I will never play pick-up basketball again.*

An activity he once loved as much as anything is now just a speck in life's unforgiving rearview mirror...*I guess it's true what people say: There's only one undefeated champ—Time.*

"CHEERS!"

Mark has just gotten home from a short driving session; his foot is throbbing. He had only been out for an hour and a half, but with his Achilles injury still on the mend, that's all the time he can put in before needing a break.

He grabs an ice pack from the freezer and wraps it around his leg when the phone rings. It's his friend Ben: A young acting buddy, who produces a lot of his own content.

Two weeks earlier, Ben had called to see if Mark would come to the set of his latest short film and take some still photos.

BEN: It's taking place in Anaheim. I can give you a $100. What do you say? It's all I've got, pal.
MARK: Not a problem, buddy. Glad to see you pursuing your dreams.
BEN: It's a shit-fest, but fuck it, right?

Mark chuckles. Out of all of his acting friends, Ben rides the emotional roller coaster most often. His highs are very high, his lows are very low, and he frequently expresses his feelings with curse words and questionable comments, but Mark knows deep inside he's just a big teddy bear, so he's happy to help. Besides, since he can't drive for long stretches, $100 sounds pretty good.

With the shoot now only two days away, he figures Ben's latest call is simply to make sure he's good to go.

MARK: Hey, buddy, what's happening?
BEN: Well, I was wondering if you could do me a little favor on Sunday besides the photography?
MARK: Sure. What's up?
BEN: Would it be possible for you to pick up George Wendt and drive him to the shoot, then take him back home when he's done?
MARK: Wait, wait, wait. You got "Norm" from *Cheers* to be in your short film?
BEN: Yep.

Knowing that Ben is also a starving actor, he finds this perplexing.

MARK: How do you always get these name actors to be in your shorts?
BEN: Ha! I like the way you said that—"In my shorts."
MARK: Your short films, Ben, your short films.
BEN: I liked it better the way you said it the first time. Although, with all due respect, I'm not sure I want George Wendt in my shorts.
MARK: Understandable. Now, how do you do it?
BEN: I just keep bugging their agents until they finally say yes.
MARK: Well done. And do you pay them?
BEN: A little. Hey, people want to work. Tough getting jobs out there.

Mark nods at the depressing thought.

BEN: So, will you do it? He lives about ten minutes from you. Just think of it as an informal Uber trip. I'll even throw in an extra twenty-five bucks.
MARK: No problem, buddy. Do you know what he's like?

BEN: Rumor is he's a curmudgeon, so you guys should get along famously.
MARK: Gee, thanks.
BEN: You know I love you, buddy.
MARK: I know. Just shoot me a text with his address and pick-up time.
BEN: You got it. See you Sunday, pal.
MARK: Yes, you will.

On Sunday, Mark arrives ten minutes early. He waits in his car for a bit, but when there's no sign of his celeb passenger, he makes his way up the front walkway. As he's approaching the house, he sees the door is open. He knocks, pokes his head in, and there's George—sitting at the kitchen table, singing, and reading the morning newspaper; he's not wearing a shirt, and it's quite possible he doesn't have pants on either.

Mark certainly doesn't care to find out and quickly turns his head away.

MARK: Uh, hi. Sorry about that.
GEORGE: You Mark? I'll be out in five.
MARK: Okay. Sounds good.

Five minutes later, George makes his way to the street, into the car, and they're off.

Conversation is minimal for the first five minutes. Mark keeps thinking about what Ben had said—"He's supposed to be a curmudgeon"—so he doesn't want to be a chatterbox nor seem like he's star struck. Eventually, however, he finds out that George started his career in Chicago.

MARK: Chicago, huh? Must have been great seeing the Cubs win the World Series last year.
GEORGE: I'm actually a White Sox fan. But I've sung "Take Me Out to the Ballgame" at Wrigley Field a bunch of times. So, yeah, good for the Cubs and good for Chicago.

The ice has been broken; their conversation doesn't slow down for the rest of the trip.

The moment they arrive on set, Ben runs up.

BEN: How'd it go?
MARK: Good.
BEN: Yeah? Did he talk at all or was he like I said?
MARK: No, he was cool. We just talked sports the whole time.
BEN: Look at that: two curmudgeons finding common ground. I appreciate it, pal.
MARK: My pleasure.

For the next few hours, Mark takes pictures of the actors in the film, and once George has finished his part, it's time to head back to L.A.

MARK: You ready to go?
GEORGE: Yep. But we're going to make a quick stop on the way back.
MARK: Uh, okay.
GEORGE: Have you ever had Portillo's?
MARK: No. What's Portillo's?

George rolls his eyes.

GEORGE: Portillo's is the home of the best hot dog and beef sandwiches you'll ever have. It's a legendary Chicago restaurant, and there just so happens to be one in Anaheim.

He looks at Mark with disgust.

GEORGE: I can't believe you've never heard of Portillo's.
MARK: Sorry.
GEORGE: Well, we're going there, and I'm buying.

Not one to ever pass up a free meal, Mark is all in.

When they arrive, George suggests using the busy drive-thru…*I wonder if he's worried about people badgering him for pictures and autographs? I suppose being an unknown actor has its benefits.*

MARK: So, what should I get?
GEORGE: Let me order for you. You like 'dogs'?
MARK: Yes.
GEORGE: You like beef sandwiches?
MARK: I guess.
GEORGE: No, "I guess," you're going to love these.
MARK: Okay.
GEORGE: So, here's what we're gonna do: We're each going to get a hot dog and eat it in the parking lot. We're also going to get a beef sandwich and save it for when we get back to L.A. They're messy and I don't want them spilling all over your car.
MARK: Thanks. You're more considerate than most of my Uber passengers.

After ordering, they wolf down their hot dogs in the parking lot. Mark thinks it was all right but nothing amazing.

GEORGE: You like it?
MARK: Yeah, it was good.
GEORGE: Well, that's just the appetizer. Once you eat that beef sandwich, you'll be forever grateful.

And with that, the two begin their trek back to Los Angeles. There's more traffic than they had encountered earlier in the day, and the conversation between them isn't as lively either, but Mark takes no umbrage.

An hour and fifteen minutes later, George is dropped off at his house.

GEORGE: Thanks. It was nice meeting you. Enjoy your sandwich.
MARK: Thanks, I'm sure I will.

Mark looks down at the cold, soggy sandwich sitting in the passenger seat—It looks horrifically unappetizing... *Best sandwich I've ever had? Doubtful.*

He takes off and heads to Pineapple Hill Saloon in Sherman Oaks to meet up with his buddy, Dan, who's in town with his wife, Sharon.

DAN: What's up Mudgey? Whatcha got there?
MARK: It's a beef sandwich from some place called Portillo's.
SHARON: Oooooo, Portillo's.
MARK: You know it?
DAN: Hell, yeah. They've got one up in San Francisco. A couple of years back, I was going through two of those a day.
MARK: That good?
DAN: Trust me, bro, you're gonna love it.

Mark's still skeptical, but he orders a beer, unwraps the soggy paper, and digs in.

The moment his taste buds meet the sandwich, all ills in the world subside.

Ohhhhhh my gosh! This is incredible!

He takes his time eating, savors every bite. Then, as he's downing the last morsel, his phone rings. He looks at the screen. The number doesn't look familiar.

MARK: I'll be right back.

He makes his way outside.

MARK: Hello?
VOICE: Hey, Mark, it's George Wendt.
MARK: Oh, hey, George. Is everything all right? Did you leave something in my car?
GEORGE: No, everything's fine. I just wanted to see how you liked your sandwich.
MARK: Oh. Um…It was actually the best sandwich I've ever had.
GEORGE: Told you.
MARK: Yes. Yes, you did.
GEORGE: Okay, well, I just wanted to see if you enjoyed it. Take care.
MARK: Yeah, um, you too, George.

He heads back into the bar.

DAN: Who was on the phone?
MARK: George Wendt. He wanted to see if I liked my sandwich.

DAN AND SHARON: Cool.
MARK: Yeah, that is pretty cool.

He grabs his beer and salutes his friends…and George Wendt.

MARK: Cheers.

"WILL BILL MIRACLES EVER CEASE?"

Mark heads out on a Thursday night. He's stressed. Acting has been slowly picking up—an audition here and there—but he knows he needs to book a role or two...*Or 7!* And soon!

Other than receiving an occasional residual check—usually only enough to treat him to a couple of tacos (nothing more)—Uber has been his lone source of income since his Achilles injury. He could really use a break. Any break.

He pulls up to his first passenger of the evening, *Bill,* who smiles as he enters the car.

BILL: Hey, how are you?
MARK: Okay, Bill. How about you?
BILL: I'm good, I'm good. Just ready to head on home.
MARK: I gotcha.
BILL: How's your day been? Have you been out driving for awhile?
MARK: I drove for about five hours this morning; I'm gonna put in a couple of hours tonight to pick up a few extra dollars.
BILL: Do you drive the late hours?
MARK: No, I try to avoid drunks.
BILL: (laughing) Understood.

The more they talk the more Mark likes Bill. He's got an easy-going demeanor, is friendly and talkative, and even cracks a few solid jokes...*Good way to start the night.*

MARK: So, what were you doing out in the Valley?
BILL: I'm working on a TV show.

Mark reflexively sits taller. Lately, almost all of his passengers have been non-talkers, so any conversation is welcomed, but talking shop for a little while would be even better.

MARK: Oh yeah, what do you do for the show?
BILL: I'm a producer.

For most people, the title "producer" would immediately raise eyebrows, thinking Bill is some big mucky-muck. But Mark knows such a proclamation can mean anything from a creative executive to a number's pusher, and rarely does the title correlate to a position as powerful as it would seem.

MARK: What kind of producer? Creative? Line producer?
BILL: I'm the Showrunner.

Hold up, wait a minute!

HE IS THE MUCKY-MUCK!!! THE CREAM OF THE CROP!!! THE BIG CHEESE!!!

Mark sits even taller, opening up like a flower being roused by the first ray of morning sunshine—for goodness sakes his last name is *Bloom!*—This is it! The miracle ride!

Okay, okay, calm down. What's the ultimate scenario?...He's working on a new show with tons of recurring roles! And...AND!...he was the showrunner on something else I've been on, so he knows my work! It's perfect! Let's do this!!!

He takes a moment, not wanting to seem overeager, and then casually—conversationally—responds.

MARK: Oh yeah, what show?
BILL: It's a show on the E! Channel called…

Noooooooooo!

The moment Mark hears "E! Channel" he need not listen any longer.

The petals of the once blooming flower fall off; his body wilts. He looks at Bill in the rearview mirror, trying with all his might to hold on to the miracle. His left eye closes—in wincing fashion—to deaden the pain that he's sure is about to come.

MARK: It's a reality show?
BILL: Yep!

Mark shakes his head and releases a guttural grunt.

MARK: Well, you're no good to me now.

Bill laughs (Mark wants to as well—he delivered the line well)…
As if that matters any longer!

Conversation ceases for the rest of the trip; Bill happily texts away while Mark gets devoured by his thoughts.

Dammit, Bill, you had so much potential. So much damn potential.

"LIFE"

It's a Monday, late afternoon. Mark has been driving most of the day. He started at 5 AM, which led to a five-and-a-half-hour morning session. Now, after a nap, shower, and some food, he's been back on the road for a few more. He's a little worn out and is hoping to hear about a role he auditioned for the previous Friday. Nothing so far, but he still senses there could be good news on the horizon. Normally, not hearing about an audition—one which he thought he had killed—would bring him down a touch (okay, more than a touch), but today is slightly different: because *today,* he is buzzing around town as a Lyft driver!

* * *

For months, Mark's friend, Sean, had been encouraging him to give Uber's rival a try.

SEAN: The passengers are cooler, they're more considerate, and they tip more often.
MARK: Yeah?
SEAN: I'm telling you, it's sooooooo much better than Uber. You'll definitely see the difference. Plus, you'll get the initial bonus to try it out.

Sean's last statement may be the most attractive portion of the pitch. Both Uber and Lyft offer bonuses to new drivers. Lyft's current promotion is $3.08 per ride up to $400. Knowing that an extra few bucks per trip adds up quickly, he's finally decided to give it a go.

After a few rides on Saturday to get the hang of the app's platform, and then an all-out effort on Sunday to really get his feet wet, he has definitely seen a difference.

Friendlier, more courteous passengers—Lyft!…Passengers frequently tipping—Lyft!!…The initial incentive of $3.08 per trip—Lyft!!!

So far, so good.

As he drives down Wilshire Blvd.—Lyft benefits swirling happily in his head—he checks the time: 4:40. He knows at 5 o'clock Santa Monica will have an automatic surge of 100% per ride, which is also a big difference from Uber, who's only offering a 30% increase.

A few minutes later, a request comes in from *Darrell.* He checks the time: 4:43…*Might as well make a few more bucks before the surge.*

He makes a left at 16th Street and lands in front of a local hospital. It's now 4:45. A woman approaches the car, opens the back door, and pokes her head in.

WOMAN: For Darrell?
MARK: Yep.
WOMAN: Hi, I'm Toni.

MARK: Hi, Toni.

She slowly makes her way into the car. Mark smiles pleasantly. As she settles in, he gets a better view of her—she looks tired.

MARK: Are you all set?
TONI: Yep.

He swipes the app and looks to see the destination.

Oh no. Oh, no-no-no!...The estimated time of the trip is one hour and thirty-four minutes.

MARK: An hour thirty-four? Where are we going?
TONI: Arcadia.

Ugh. There goes my 100% surge. You're killing me, Toni.

TONI: Sorry we're going so far. Is that all right?
MARK: (swallowing his words) Yep, no problem.

He sighs an almighty sigh, pulls away from the curb, and they begin their journey.

Within a block, Toni begins talking non-stop. She bombards Mark with questions, none of which he can answer because the moment he starts, she's peppering him with another. Her body is just as hyper: She rocks in her seat and taps the headrest in front of her like a drummer warming up for a set. Her fidgety state is beginning to make Mark feel a little anxious himself...*This is going to be a very, very long trip—literally and figuratively.*

Finally, for the briefest of moments, Toni stops talking. She sits back. Her body sinks into her seat.

TONI: I apologize for yammering on so much. Things have been a little crazy, and today has been tough on me.
MARK: Oh?
TONI: Yes. You see, my son was killed in a car accident awhile back; tomorrow would have been his birthday.

Mark's heart drops into his stomach.

MARK: Oh my gosh. I'm so sorry, Toni.
TONI: Thanks. He was hit by a guy running a red at sixty-five miles per hour. My son walked off the sidewalk and was killed instantly. And would you believe, the guy driving only got nineteen days in jail.
MARK: What? How is that possible?
TONI: It's the way the laws are written. He gets nineteen days, and all I'm left with is the memory of the last conversation I had with my son, five minutes before he died.

A morbid air takes over, but when Mark peeks in the rearview mirror, he's surprised to see a little twinkle in Toni's eye. The corners of her lips have risen ever so slightly and her whole body has calmed down...*She's probably thinking about her son.*

But soon thereafter, she pops forward again, taps the back of the passenger seat, and continues to reveal her story.

TONI: To make matters worse, my husband of twenty-six years is now divorcing me. I guess that's common in tragedies like this. Plus, I just recently got past cancer, but now I need to have

surgery on my knee. I've had to come to the hospital four times over this past week.
MARK: Oh, wow. Do you have to take Lyft each time?
TONI: Uber, Lyft, whatever. My friend Darrell orders the rides for me. I see you've got stickers for both.

She points at his windshield.

MARK: I do have both. But the truth is—and please don't tell anybody this—I'm just trying to get as many stickers as I can so that chicks will think I'm a NASCAR driver.

He winks, and Toni howls with delight.

MARK: I actually just started with Lyft on Saturday.
TONI: Really? How is it?

He explains the differences between the two companies and notices that Toni is engrossed with everything he says.

As the ride continues, and their conversation balances out, Toni leans forward in her seat now and then to be fully engaged—her smile becomes more and more present each time she does so.

During the ride the two discuss everything under the sun: politics, sports, the letter Toni wrote to the man who killed her son, the experiences each had growing up in Los Angeles, different GPS apps, the colon cancer she survived.

Everything.

Every once in a while, Mark refers to her as "kid" or "young lady"; she gets a kick out of it.

TONI: I like it when you say that.
MARK: Good. I have a friend who gets really upset whenever I call her "kid" or if I say "atta-girl."
TONI: Well, that's silly. It's endearing. She should appreciate it.
MARK: That's what I keep telling her!

They both laugh. In fact, they laugh a lot during the ride.

Mark finds Toni's resiliency to be amazing. She is upbeat throughout—even when the discussion shifts to deep and painful subjects—and her personality is fun and playful...*Is it a defense mechanism or is she actually this optimistic? I guess it doesn't really matter, just glad she's enjoying herself.*

They make their way off the freeway and begin weaving through the streets of Arcadia. The sun is setting; the neighborhood is peaceful and quiet.

They turn onto Toni's street.

TONI: The one on the right, where the blue car is parked. That's my husband's. He hasn't moved out yet.

Mark checks the rearview mirror; Toni's transfixed on the car. For the briefest of moments, he believes he sees her jovial attitude slip. But then—just as quickly—she diverts her eyes, regroups, and rediscovers her positive outlook.

They stop in front of her house. Mark twists to her. She begins typing out a text.

TONI: I'm going to make sure Darrell leaves you a good tip.

Mark laughs in his throat while his nose flares, allowing air to flow more freely as he attempts to fight back the emotions that are swelling within him.

MARK: That's very sweet, Toni, but don't worry about that. It's not a big deal.
TONI: No, no. He always asks me, "How was the driver?" I'm going to tell him how nice you were. How you called me "kid" and "young lady"—I really liked that—and to give you a big tip.

She finishes her text and looks to him and smiles.

TONI: I'm glad I got you as my driver. It was a lot of fun. Thanks for all the conversation.

He nods, accepting her appreciation. He appreciates her too. Instinctively, he puts out his hand; hers falls gently into his. Their fingers intertwine for just a few seconds—it doesn't need to be any longer.

MARK: You're a doll, Toni. I wish you all the best.
TONI: Thanks.

She smiles at him one last time, then exits to whatever the future holds.

Mark watches her disappear behind the front door. He slouches and takes in a deep breath. He thinks about the encounter. Tears well up in his eyes.

Well, buddy, I'd say today you truly did your job…Lift.

"Everything."

★★★★★

"ROLLER COASTER—OOO-OO-OO-OO-OOO—ROLLER COASTER"

Mark's been driving since six in the morning. It's now eleven. He's worn out and hungry.

He walks into a Toluca Lake café, scans the room, spots the person he's looking for, and then makes a beeline for his old friend, Eric. The two give each other a hearty hug.

ERIC: How long's it been?
MARK: I was wondering the same thing. I think around twenty-five years.
ERIC: Yeah, probably.

The two have an interesting relationship; they have never been super close, yet they still have a bond: Some of Eric's closest high school friends became some of Mark's closest college friends. And it was during Eric's visits to see his high school buddies at UCSB that he and Mark met.

They also share one other commonality: Both have been entertainers throughout their adult lives. Fortunately, for Eric, he hasn't had to ride the same roller coaster as Mark. Oh, he's certainly had his dips and turns, highs and lows, but during his entire adult life, he's been able to make a living by being the frontman for various bands. For years, he's toured Northern California, entertaining people nearly every weekend. And while Mark knows that Eric is also grinding, he's still a little jealous, wishing he, too, didn't need side jobs to make ends meet.

Today, they are reuniting because Eric is in town to visit his daughter, who is about to graduate from AMDA—a local college for the Performing Arts. He's asked Mark to give her the lowdown on what it's like to be an actor in L. A.

MARK: You know I'm not going to sugarcoat it, right?
ERIC: I don't want you to. I want her to know what she's getting into. We both know that being an artist isn't for the faint of heart. Lay it on thick.
MARK: (laughing) I think telling her that I haven't booked a role in seven months will be thick enough.
ERIC: No doubt.

They sit down, Mark meets Eric's daughter, and then—just as he is about to roll out the truth carpet—his phone rings.

MARK: Oh, hey, it's my manager. Excuse me for one second.

He makes his way outside.

MARK: Hello?
HANK: Bloomin' Onion, watcha doin'?
MARK: Just about to have breakfast with an old friend and his daughter. She wants to be an actress. I'm going to give her my thoughts on the business.
HANK: Hmmm. Interesting timing…

A minute later, Mark walks back in.

ERIC: Everything okay?
MARK: Yep, I just booked a role on *NCIS Los Angeles.*

He looks over at Eric's daughter. Her eyes are bugging out and a 20,000-watt smile shines from her face.

MARK: No, no, no, young lady; do not get the wrong idea. This is not the way Hollywood usually works.

The following week he is on the set of *NCIS Los Angeles*, ready to do his scene. Sitting on the other side of a conference table is his scene partner, Todd Smith—a.k.a. LL Cool J… *Whatever you do, do not call him LL or Mr. Cool J or…Just don't say anything if you don't have to.*

It's a fun role with comedic moments that Mark milks. The crew is getting a kick out of the back and forth between him and Todd that's being accentuated by a little improvised "double hand tap" that the two are playing off of one another. It's a small bit, but the director definitely finds it adds color to the scene and he keeps encouraging them to go with it.

Within a couple of hours, Mark has completed his role, and he searches out Todd.

MARK: I just wanted to say thanks for having me on the show. Mr…Um…uh…Thanks for having me.

TODD: No problem. And, hey—that little knock-knock thing worked.

Mark grins.
MARK: Uh, yeah, it definitely did. Take care.

He turns and, once out of view, pumps his fist.

A half hour later, he's making his way out to the Paramount Studio parking lot with one of the other day players, Rich, whom he bonded with during the shoot.

RICH: So, he said the knock-knock bit worked, huh?
MARK: Yeah.
RICH: Well, he was right. Everyone was laughing each time you guys did it. It was a funny scene, man.
MARK: Thanks. You definitely killed your stuff. It should all come together nicely.
RICH: Absolutely...Well, this is me.

Rich points to an expensive new car.

MARK: Oh. Um, that's nice.
RICH: Thanks. Where you at?

Mark points to his car, which hasn't been washed in a month. The white Uber sticker stands out from all the dirt.

RICH: You Uber?
MARK: Yep, gotta.

Rich takes this in.

RICH: Well, keep grinding, brother. Hopefully, we'll work together again someday.

MARK: Sounds good.

They hug it out and go their separate ways.

As Mark enters his car, he feels the day's luster quickly losing its shine...*It's okay. He was a cool dude. Maybe you won't have to drive too much longer. But in the meantime...*

He prompts the app and begins taking requests. After two rides he's had enough, and he begins making his way home—satisfied with the extra $11.15 he's made.

As he stops at a red light on Gower St.—the iconic Hollywood Sign rising as a sign of hope in the distant mountains in front of him—his phone rings.

MARK; Hey, Mariko.
MARIKO: Hey, MB. How'd it go today?
MARK: Really good. It was a lot of fun.
MARIKO: Great. Well, since you had so much fun on that, want to have some fun on *The Mindy Project* too?
MARK: Um, sure.
MARIKO: Good, because you just booked a role for next week.

He smiles, looks at the Uber sticker, looks at the Hollywood Sign, looks at himself in the rearview mirror, and then laughs...*My goodness, what a roller coaster.*

"THE RATINGS GAME"

Mark gets up early on a Saturday morning and bounces out of his apartment. Since booking *NCIS Los Angeles* and *The Mindy Project*, his spirits have been much higher. Not only was he pleased to have gotten some work for a change, but it also thrilled him to have finally landed his first gigs since signing with the new management team. Admittedly, he was beginning to put pressure on himself in his quest to prove his worth to them.

His recent good fortune has also improved his demeanor when driving. Consequently, his Uber rating has been steadily rising.

As he gets in his car, he checks his rating...*4.97! Wow, my all-time high! Okay, then! Let's go make some money and make people happy!*

Soon thereafter, he pulls up to the Universal Hilton and picks up *Sherry* and a companion. They are headed to a small hotel in Hollywood.

From the exterior, the hotel doesn't seem like much, but the last time Mark was there, he was greeted by a security perimeter a city block wide. His car was searched, and his driver's license was given a background check by the Secret Service. *The* Secret Service.

MARK: Ya know, the last time I was here the Secret Service was doing security checks just to pull up to the hotel.

SHERRY: Oh, that's nice.

Sherry's response is short and dismissive, and she quickly reengages with her colleague. Just as quickly, Mark feels subservient. He descends into a bitter mood…*Hey!!! I just did a great scene with L.L. Cool J! Top that, Sherry!!!*…A list of accomplishments stack up in his head...*I'm a college graduate. I've written numerous screenplays. I had my own comic strip. Um…um…and other stuff too! I'm smart and interesting, and I donate blood regularly, dammit!*

His thoughts have gone full on *Fatal Attraction...I won't be ignored, Sherry!*

He stews in his own juice and remains quiet for the next ten minutes.

As they approach the hotel—stopping at a red light across the street from the front entrance—Sherry leans forward.

SHERRY: There's a driveway on the left where you can drop us off.

He rolls his eyes, shakes his head, and then speaks like "Lenny" in the movie *Of Mice and Men.*

MARK: Ohhhhhh. You mean where that sign is?
SHERRY: Yes, where the sign is.
MARK: Can you see what it says?
SHERRY: "Hotel parking entrance."
MARK: Oh, thank you. I don't do so good at reading, ya know.

He glances in the rearview mirror. Daggers are shooting from Sherry's eyes.

MARK: Just kidding.

A minute later, he drops off Sherry and her companion—bereft of thank yous and your welcomes—then pulls over on a side street. There, he scans the app. Oh, he knows the answer to what he's searching for, but he still has to check. He presses the prompt that displays his driver rating...*4.96.*

He smiles...*So worth it.*

"Super Professional"

★★★★★

"THE SUIT"

OCTOBER 6, 2017

Mark is standing outside his apartment building on a late Friday afternoon. A rare look of confidence rides upon his face. Perhaps it's what's in store for him later in the evening that's making him stand a little taller. Perhaps it's his recent bookings and a handful of other solid auditions that has made him puff out his chest ever so slightly. And perhaps his confidence has peaked simply because he's wearing *The Suit.*

Dubbed by his budz, Kim, *The Suit* is a dark purple Hugo Boss ensemble that Mark found on sale a few years earlier, and one which seems to have magical powers. Multiple times he has worn *The Suit* to an audition and booked the role. He's had passersby gawk at him while wearing *The Suit.* And the ultimate sign of its unearthly capabilities was when he and Kim were shooting an experimental short film on the Santa Monica Pier and seemingly every female walking by—no matter their age—stared at him like he was the sexiest man-beast to ever walk the planet.

KIM: You need to wear that more often; women are literally stopping in their tracks to stare at you.
MARK: I know, this is bizarre. I don't know what's going on.
KIM: Yo, money! It's gotta be *the suit!*

At the time he simply laughed at Kim's Spike Lee/Mars Blackmon imitation, but over the years it's become near impossible for him to deny how generous *The Suit* has been. He's also done his best to not abuse *The Suit's* mystical properties—pulling it from his closet only on special occasions.

Tonight's event, however, is worthy of an appearance. Because tonight—at 50 years, 8 months, 16 days, and a handful of hours—for the first time ever, Mark will get to watch himself in a feature film.

Yes, *School Spirits* is having its long-awaited premiere. And while the film is set for a digital release—and will only play in a theater on this night—he is still exhilarated.

As he waits for his Uber to arrive, he thinks about his mom, who is being picked up and driven to the screening by his cousin, Lori and her husband, Jonathan. Watching her son struggle—both creatively and financially—over the years hasn't been easy on her. But tonight she'll get to share in the joyous experience, making the barren years feel much more fruitful and worthwhile...*Just wish dad could be here too.*

Along with the screening itself, there's one other thing Mark's looking forward to: the ride over. He thinks about all the weddings, concerts, and sporting events he's pulled up to, and how he's watched intoxicatingly excited passengers spill from his car with laughter, allured by an evening full of good times... *Well, tonight I'm going to be that drunk from excitement passenger, and I'm going to enjoy every single turn and moment along the way.*

Ronnie pulls up in a freshly washed Civic.

MARK: Hey, Ronnie. Thanks for coming to get me. Do you mind if I sit in the front seat?
RONNIE: No problem; whatever you prefer.

He gets in, Ronnie swipes the app, and they are on their way.

RONNIE: So, what do you have going on tonight?
MARK: I'm heading to a film premiere.
RONNIE: Oh, yeah? Nice. Are you involved in the movie in some way?
MARK: Yeah, I acted in it. It's actually the biggest role I've ever had.
RONNIE: Well, shoot, good for you!
MARK: Thanks.
RONNIE: And I've gotta say: you definitely look the part. That suit you're wearing is sharp.

Mark chuckles, looks down at *The Suit,* and smiles knowingly.

MARK: Thanks, Ronnie. I like it too.

"Ronnie was kind, a fantastic driver, and has great taste in men's apparel."

"HOLLOW-EEN"

It's Halloween Night and Mark decides—against his better judgement—to go out and make some money. Yes, surges will be very high, but the possibility of picking up drunk passengers, obnoxious passengers, discourteous passengers is also very high...*I guess we'll see what happens.*

His first pick up is in Burbank. There's a little surge and two guys dressed as superheroes get in the car. They're somewhat rambunctious, but nice, and with traffic still pretty light, it's an easy twenty-minute drive into Hollywood.

*Okay, that was wasn't so bad. Maybe this will work out...*Five minutes later, he picks up two more men. One is dressed as Frankenstein and the other is dressed as...*I have no idea what that is, but as long as they're cool, I really don't care.*

Again, his passengers are lively but friendly. Mark swipes and sees they are heading to the Valley.

MARK: That's unusual.
FRANKENSTEIN: What's that?
MARK: Oh, nothing really. It's just that I'm always taking people from the Valley into the City, but I never take people from the

City into the Valley. Frankly, I don't even know how those people ever get home.

Indecipherable Guy groans and elbows Frankenstein.

INDECIPHERABLE GUY: See?!

Frankenstein brushes off his buddy.

FRANKENSTEIN: (to Mark) We've got a party to go to.
MARK: I get it. It's just unusual. No one goes to the Valley to party.
INDECIPHERABLE GUY: *See?!*
FRANKENSTEIN: I promise we'll take off if it's lame.
INDECIPHERABLE GUY: It's in the Valley, of course it's gonna be lame.

Everyone laughs and Mark is given a five-dollar tip.

MARK: Thanks, guys. Have fun.
INDECIPHERABLE GUY: We'll try.
FRANKENSTEIN: Don't mind him. Have a good night. Drive safe.

Soon another request comes in...*Okay then, let's do this.*

Minutes later, Mark is slowly making his way down a dark, quiet street. It's difficult for him to see any addresses, but as he continues to inch forward, two early twenty-something *Dudes* bound out of a house on the left. They're hyped, they're rowdy, they're not alone. As they reach the car, two more dudes come bouncing out of the house. All the dudes are dressed alike, but like before, Mark doesn't understand what their costumes represent...*Are they male strippers? Are they Zombies?...Zombie Strippers, perhaps.*

Dude #1 makes it into the car and calls out to his fellow bros.

DUDE #1: Yo, dudes, let's go!

Dude #2 almost takes a seat, but after opening his door, he stops, looks back to the house, and yells out to Dudes 3 and 4.

DUDE #2: Yo, get the cologne!
DUDE #3: Gotcha, bro.

Dudes 3 and 4 quickly reverse course. However, Dude #2 doesn't believe Dudes 3 and 4 will be able to find the cologne by themselves, so he, too, heads back to the house, leaving his door wide open in the process.

MARK: Hey, can you…Never mind.

Soon, Dude #1 starts to feel lonely—at least that's Mark's assumption—because just like Dudes 2-4, he also heads back whence he came…*At least he shut his door.*

As Dude #1 makes his way into the house, Mark shakes his head and bites down on his lip. Up to this point no Dudes have even acknowledged their patient driver. No "What's up, bro?"…No "Just give us a second, bro."…No "How do you like my Zombie Stripper costume, bro?"…Nada!

A minute passes. A second minute passes. A third minute passes… No Dudes.

Mark lets out a sigh, casually gets out of the car, and shuts the back door. He then sits back down, straps his seat belt, and takes off.

As he is leaving, he notices the Dudes making their way out of the house, but it's too late: The trip has been cancelled.

As he's zooming down the street, he looks in the rearview mirror and sees four Zombie Stripper Dudes emphatically waving their arms. It puts a grin on his face...*Sorry, bros. Try being a little more courteous next time.*

He turns off the app, heads home, watches *Sportscenter,* and happily falls asleep on his couch a whole twenty dollars richer.

"Happy Halloween!"

★★★★★

"THE DROP"

Mark has just dropped off a passenger in the heart of downtown. Mark hates downtown. Not that he hates the area as a whole, he just hates downtown as an Uber driver. One-way streets, mass construction, difficulty locating passengers, and horrible traffic makes it very tough on ride share drivers. Since it's a Tuesday night at 9:15, he's finding the usual obstacles to be a little less troubling...But he still wants to get out of there.

The app chimes, and he talks himself into accepting the request... *Hopefully, it will take you towards home. Maybe you'll even have a nice conversation.*

He pulls up to where he thinks his passenger, *Carlos,* should be waiting, but no passersby are making their way to his car, and he can't locate any addresses... *Why can't they make the numbers enormous so they're easy to find?!*

He shakes his head and waits. Seconds later, a man comes out of a dark, bland building, carrying a medium-sized plastic bag. He motions for Mark to roll down the passenger window.

MARK: Carlos?
MAN: No, you're going to see Carlos.

The man tosses the bag through the open window and onto the passenger seat.

MARK: What's this?
MAN: It's what you're going to take to Carlos.

While Mark has delivered packages in the past, he's never been handed one at night in front of a (now) sketchy downtown building.

MARK: Yo, I don't even know what's in this. I'm not taking this.
MAN: It's just sweatshirts, bro.
MARK: Just sweatshirts?

The man nods. Mark looks to the bag. There is, in fact, a sweatshirt sitting at the very top. He sighs, shakes his head, and—despite every cell in his body telling him to cancel the trip—reluctantly agrees.

MARK: All right, fine.
MAN: Thanks, bro.

The man walks away...*So much for a good conversation.*

He swipes the app. The map reveals that he'll be heading out of downtown—but South—and away from home. He sighs and begins the estimated twenty-five-minute trek.

Within minutes of crossing the 10 Freeway, he notices the roads becoming more and more desolate—there's less traffic, apartment buildings are morphing into factories, streetlights are rare.

Where the hell am I going?...Fuckin' Carlos...No. How about fuckin' Mark?! Why did you accept this trip? You should have just told the guy you don't do drops. Fuck.

The road gets darker, quieter. A train's horn blows into the night. Mark jumps from the noise and practically breaks his seat belt.

MARK: FUCK!!!
GPS: (Pleasant female voice) Make a right turn.
MARK: Finally!

He turns and pulls up to a red light. There's only one other car nearby; it's directly in front of him. They stay stopped for what seems like an eternity...*Come on, come on...*

Then.

GUNSHOT!...A FRIGGIN' GUNSHOT!

Mark slouches and attempts to hide behind the steering wheel (as if that'll do any good). He scans the area while praying for the light to change.

Are you fuckin' kidding me??? Fuck you, Uber, you don't care. Fuck you, Carlos, you don't care.

He looks at the bag of sweatshirts. Eyes them.

Fuck you, too!!

The light changes. The car in front of him pulls over to the side of the road.

Mark nervously drives past.

Please don't be the one with the gun-Please don't be the one with the gun-Please don't be the one with the gun.

GPS: Make a left turn.

He quickly pulls at the wheel, only to find himself on an empty street: not a single car is parked, not a single person is seen, brick buildings line both sides. He slows down and cranes his neck forward, desperately trying to find the address. The street is darker than dark; that isn't helping either, but the GPS says he's close, so he slows to a crawl.

GPS: (pleasant voice) You've arrived.
MARK: I've arrived?!? I've arrived *where?!?*—My life's ending?!?
GPS: (pleasant-mocking-voice) You've arrived.
MARK: *SHUT UP!!!*

He grabs his phone, calls Carlos. No one answers.

Fuck this. If no one is out here in thirty seconds, I'm throwing the bag out the window and I'm gone. 30, 29, 28, 27…

The phone rings.

MARK: Hello?!
VOICE: Mark, it's Carlos. Are you here?
MARK: I have no friggin' idea where I am. The GPS says I'm here, but I see no addresses or any people.
CARLOS: I'll be right out.
MARK: You've got thirty seconds or I'm throwing this bag out the window.

CARLOS: I'll be right out.

Mark grumbles some more, then spots a silhouetted figure running towards him.

This better be fuckin' Carlos.

He rolls down the window, bag in hand, ready to throw it at whoever is sliding up to his car.

The man gets to the window.

CARLOS: Mark?

Mark looks around at his surroundings…*Are you kidding me?!? Who else do you think I am, Sherlock??? I'm the only car on the street, and there's an Uber sticker on my windshield!! Who do you think I am?—The friggin' Sweatshirt Fairy?!?!?*

He nods without saying a word.

CARLOS: Thanks, bro.

Carlos grabs the bag of sweatshirts and falls back into the shadows. Meanwhile, Mark makes a screechy U-turn and retraces his steps back to where he feels comfortable, safe, and happy…

Downtown.

"Excellent Service"

★★★★★

"THE CITY OF ANGELS"

It's a cloudy, dreary day and the City of Los Angeles is in trouble; there's a monster roaming the streets. It's angry and reactionary and could terrorize unsuspecting neighborhoods at any moment. Yes, there's a monster out there all right, and its name is *Grumpy Mark.*

Oh yeah, Mark is definitely in a pissy mood, and driving around L.A. is what's soured his disposition. Half the drivers are speeding and cutting off others; the remaining half are stuck in the middle of intersections because their green light has turned red and they had already made their way halfway through, thinking that traffic would've cleared by the time the light had changed—it hasn't... *Good job, buddy! Now no one can go anywhere!*...It's a sea of narcissism. Drivers are paying more attention to their cell phone, Starbucks coffee, and the tiny dog lying in their laps than the cars surrounding them; the entire city is honking at one another, and to make matters worse, every one of Mark's passengers has been rude and unappreciative.

As he drops off another egocentric rider, who apparently couldn't connect the words "thank" and "you" if his life depended on it, he has had enough. He rolls down the passenger window.

MARK: Hey, buddy, I think you forgot something.

The passenger turns, makes his way back to the car, and—for the first time since the trip began—acknowledges Mark's being.

PASSENGER: I did?
MARK: Yeah, you forgot to say thanks.

The man glares.

MARK: You're welcome.

Mark pulls away, leaving the inconsiderate rider standing frozen on the sidewalk... *Yeah, probably won't be getting a tip on that one.*

He thinks about going home right then and there, but when he hears that all too familiar chime, he accepts another trip.

He reaches to swipe the app, and as he does so, something remarkable happens: The dreary clouds above part ever so slightly, allowing a single, sharp ray of sunlight to squeeze through and strike the street like a spotlight hitting a stage... *Interesting*... He shakes his head and looks down at the app to get the details of the pickup location. As he sees the address, he notices something else intriguing. He looks a little closer... *Could it be?*

Quickly he navigates through traffic. He makes two rights, one left, and sure enough, standing elegantly on the sidewalk is a woman brimming with confidence and joyful energy—*it's Yazmin.*

Before she can even say hello, he breaks the ice.

MARK: Well, I know you!
YAZMIN: You do?
MARK: Yep. I had you as a passenger one time.

YAZMIN Really?! That's wild!
MARK: You had a commercial callback, and you were running late. You told me how you performed spoken word and we each recited a piece.
YAZMIN: Oh my gosh!!! I totally remember that! What are the odds I would get you as a driver again?!
MARK: (laughing) Not very good.

And it's true: With millions of people living in Los Angeles, and thousands upon thousands of them being ride share drivers, the odds of having the same connection is pretty slim—especially when the two pickup locations are ten miles apart.

During the ride, they catch up like long-lost friends, and Yazmin takes a video for Snapchat.

YAZMIN: Hey, guys, you won't believe this: I got the same Uber driver that I had once before. Say hey, Mark.
MARK: Hey!

As they pull up to her spot, she finishes the video.

YAZMIN: Wow, that was crazy. It was great seeing you again.
MARK: Likewise. Maybe I'll be lucky enough to have you as a passenger again someday.
YAZMIN: Ya never know. Take care now.
MARK: You too.

She leaves with a laugh and a wave, and Mark drives off with a huge smile on his face.

A moment later, he makes a right turn, glances over to the side of the road and sees a colorfully painted sculpture of an angel. Years earlier, Los Angeles had commissioned several artists to paint similar pieces. They adorned many of the streets of L.A. with vibrancy and life. There's only a few remaining now, but Mark still enjoys seeing the vivid works of art whenever he comes across one.

I guess it just goes to show you: Los Angeles has its tough, potholed days, but there's always the possibility of finding an angel when you least expect it.

He smiles and looks to the (now) blue sky above... *Thanks, Yazmin. You'll truly never know how much you made my day.*

"PROFESSIONAL CONFESSIONALS"

THANKSGIVING 2017

Thanksgiving has always been Mark's favorite holiday. It was the one day each year where the entire family got together. Truth is, when he was growing up there wasn't all that much quality family time. With his father frequently traveling and his mom trying to keep up with her sons' mismatched schedules, it was rare to have a family dinner with all five members present.

But Thanksgiving was different. His aunt, uncle, and cousins would come over, and it gave everyone an opportunity to bond. Each year he looked forward to the last Thursday of November and that family connection—even if it was only for a few hours.

Years later, Thanksgiving celebrations moved from Los Angeles to San Diego after Mark's parents and oldest brother, Jeff, settled there. For the last twenty years, the family has gotten together at Jeff and his wife, Teri's, house. And this year, as Mark and his mom drive south from L.A., he's hoping those childhood feelings of "family" are rekindled.

It helps that he's in a good mood: his Achilles injury has continued to heal, he's looking forward to seeing his brilliant nieces, and he's in a good state of mind when it comes to his career. Just a couple of days prior, he was pinned for a recurring guest star on a legal drama, *and* he's gotten word that his character on *NCIS Los Angeles* is most likely going to be written into another episode... *This could be it. This could be what you've always worked for.*

However, despite the positives—and looking forward to a much-needed break from L.A.—he knows that Thanksgiving weekends will never be the same. The holiday has become a mixed bag of emotions for the entire family, and he now finds it difficult to separate good from bad.

He looks over at his mom and can't help but wonder what is going through her mind. It's been three years now and so much has changed...

Thanksgiving Day, 2014, begins in typical fashion with Mark making an early morning drive to San Diego. However, instead of heading straight to his parents' house—before caravanning to Jeff's—he first makes a hospital visit to see his ailing dad. For the previous two years, his dad's health has been in decline. Lately he's been living at the hospital more often than at home. His most recent malady is a blood infection, but there are also issues with his heart, and he has a terrible case of gout, which has spread throughout his body, leaving him in terrible agony most of the time. Only a few things are keeping him going: his strong will, a positive attitude, and his love for his family.

He smiles when Mark enters the room.

DAD: Hey there. How was your drive down?
MARK: It was fine. How are you doing?

DAD: All right. Just another day in the hospital. I'll be in here all weekend, and I'm going to have to go into a care facility for awhile once they get the infection under control.
MARK: I know, I heard. Thanksgiving won't be the same without you at the table.
DAD: Well, make sure you enjoy yourselves, anyway.

He forces a smile, not wanting to be the reason for anyone to have a melancholy holiday.

MARK: Hey, I brought you something.
DAD: Yeah?

Mark pulls out a wrapped present and opens the package, revealing a book.

DAD: Oh, wow. It's the comic strip you used to write.
MARK: Yep. I compiled them all just for you. I know how much you enjoyed them; although, I think you may have been the only one.
DAD: (laughing) Stop that. It's a terrific strip. I could never understand why it didn't catch on.

Mark shrugs as his father reads the cover.

DAD: *Fans-See This!* I will love reading these again. Thank you so much.
MARK: My pleasure.

Mark props up the book and turns the pages—the pain from the gout is too much for his dad to hold the book by himself. After a few minutes, the task seems futile.

DAD: Why don't we stop for now. We can try again a little later.

MARK: Of course; whatever you want.

That afternoon the family celebrates Thanksgiving at Jeff's house. It's still a pleasant day, but not the same without the patriarch of the family at the table.

The rest of the weekend involves family activities and dropping by the hospital. On Sunday morning, Mark is set to head back to Los Angeles, but before driving home, he stops in to see how his dad is feeling.

MARK: Hi, how are you doing?
DAD: Not good. It's over.

Oh no.

They've had this conversation before—his dad expressing how he didn't want to live any longer if this is what life would be like. The pain, especially from the gout, has become too much. Even the slightest touch causes him to writhe, and basic mobility has become a major issue.

DAD: I want to stop all medications. It's time. I've lived a good life. It's okay.
MARK: Um…okay…Well, look: Mom and Jeff are on their way over; let's talk about it with them when they get here.

Just then the doctor arrives.

DOCTOR: Hello, Mr. Bloom. How are you feeling?
DAD: Not good.

Mark pulls her aside.

MARK: He's ready to die. He wants to go out on his own terms.
DOCTOR: I understand. Unfortunately, his white count has elevated. The antibiotics aren't working. I'm very sorry. I like your dad. I can tell he's a good man. We will do everything we can to make him comfortable.

Mark tears up.

MARK: Thank you. *He is a good man.*

Over the next couple of days, the family gathers around the hospital bed. Stories are shared, there are laughs, smiles, and tears. Mark's dad gently sways his head back and forth as they play some of his favorite music in the background. While the rest of the family can keep it together, Mark cannot. He often excuses himself to find empty areas of the lobby or hides behind large potted plants and cries non-stop.

Along with his mom, he sleeps at the hospital for the next two nights and takes some time to write out his thoughts on his dad's life. On Tuesday, he drives to his parent's home to take a shower and get himself together. On the way back to the hospital, Jeff calls.

MARK: Hey.
JEFF: Hey, buddy…I'm sorry; I know you wanted to be here, but Dad just passed.

He pulls over to the side of the road, heartbroken, but relieved his dad is no longer uncomfortable. Ten minutes later, he arrives at the hospital, touches his dad's hand, thankful it no longer causes him pain, and kisses his forehead.

MARK: Thanks for everything, Pop. I couldn't have asked for anything more from a father. You're the best.

He glances up and sees the *Fans-See This!* book sitting unopened on the nightstand. His stomach clenches.

Sorry. I wish I would have gotten it to you sooner.

He contacts relatives and friends, finishes writing the tribute to his dad, and then posts it on his Facebook page.

> This morning, my dad passed away at the age of 85. I wasn't sure if I wanted to write about his life. Instead, I thought I'd just post a simple note to let friends know. But the more I thought about it, the more I realized that few of my friends knew him, so I guess I've decided to give it a go. I'll probably forget some stuff and kick myself later, but how can you summarize all that he did in 85 years? So, I'll just say, here's a little bit about my dad...
>
> Leon Bloom was born on January 3, 1929 and grew up in Brighton Beach, NY. In those Brooklyn streets he played stickball, rooted for the Yankees, and DiMaggio was his guy. He also loved to sing and was a huge Sinatra fan. Later in life, he often sang at piano bars.
>
> My dad was an excellent student and went to the prestigious high school, Brooklyn Tech. Later, he

was drafted and served in the Army during the Korean War. He then moved to L.A. where he met my mom, Renee. They got married soon after and have been together for 61 years. I literally never once saw my folks argue. They were meant for each other. So much so, that—other than setting them up on their first date—they each couldn't stand the guy who introduced them. They were terrific swing dance and bridge partners, and they worked tirelessly to provide love and support for their three sons—and we were not easy sons to raise. However, both my dad and mom were always there for us, especially supporting us in our chosen fields.

For work, he was a computer designer and teamed up with colleagues to come up with some of the most important and innovative computer concepts of its time, including the ASCII system, which is still used today.

My dad was always a straight shooter—honest to a fault (hmmmmm? sounds familiar). He led by example, rather than words. He had a very dry sense of humor—another familiarity—and was always politically cognizant. You know how people say "If you're not happy write your Congressman"?—Well my dad did. He wrote to the President, Senators, Congressmen, and local and national papers all the time. He also wrote a novel, a musical, and numerous poems for my mom, amongst other things.

Obviously, there are many things I am proud of, but perhaps mostly, it was what he did in his retirement. For eighteen years, three to five days a week, he volunteered at a local school and worked with kids who had trouble learning, only stopping when his health prevented him from continuing. He also led the local World Affairs Council where they discussed the events of the day. Climate Change was the subject he found to be most important. He frequently gave lectures on the issue.

Plus, after the President of the Community Concert Series was caught embezzling money, my Dad took over that job, too! For the next half-dozen years, he found the acts, took care of marketing and sales, and eventually had a surplus of money in the thousands, which was donated to the local high school for instruments and college scholarships. All the while he was being a wonderful husband, father, and grandfather.

In his last years, his main goal was to implement an interactive teaching system for schools, primarily with lower-income communities in mind.

Dad cheated death a few times—twice from cancer and once, remarkably, from a burst aorta. I believe he was meant to live longer for the purpose of giving back.

Unfortunately—as we all shall experience—his life has come to an end. He faced his final days with courage, love, humor, and compassion towards others—frequently reminding his loved ones surrounding his bed that the most important thing is love and peace. To be giving, sympathetic, and provide goodness to your fellow man (especially the poor) as well as the planet.

For the most part, the last two days were wonderful. The room was full of love, laughter, and stories. My father was fully lucid during this time and soaked it all in, saying frequently, "It couldn't have ended any better."

Finally, I'll just say that he requested none of us say "goodbye"—it sounded too final for him. So, Dad, I'll just say, thanks for everything. I'll miss you but will always be reminded of you, and we'll catch up somewhere down the road.

Love,
Mudge

Responses pour in. Mark reads them to his mom. They both find comfort in them.

He spends the next ten days in San Diego and does whatever he can to help her, although she is as strong as an elephant. At no time does she cry. In fact, Mark has never seen his mom cry…*ever.*

MARK: You know, Mom, you can release your emotions. It's okay.
MOM: I know, but I don't cry.
MARK: But it's okay to do so.
MOM: I know.

She pauses for a moment.

MOM: Do you know why I don't?
MARK: No.

Again, she pauses. A recollection fills her entire soul.

MOM: When I was a little girl, I came home sobbing one day, and my mother said, "You're not allowed to cry. Only children in the Holocaust are allowed to cry."...It was the last time I ever did.

Mark is floored. It's the first time he's heard the story.

MARK: Well, Mom, I'm giving you permission to cry if you want to. I'm sure the children from the Holocaust would understand.

They smile at one another: one of only a few moments of joy they've been able to elicit over the past week.

A few days later, she approaches him.

MOM: You need to go home. I appreciate everything, but you have a life to live, and I'm doing just fine.

They hug, and the next day he heads back to L.A.

Over the next couple of months, he splits his time between Los Angeles and San Diego. She has decided to sell her home and move to L.A., where she'll share an apartment with Mark's middle brother. Along with Jeff and Teri, he does all he can to help get the house in order, organize the move, and spend time with her.

MARK: I've always loved you. You know that, right?

MOM: Yes.
MARK: But I don't really think we've ever been super close.
MOM: I agree.
MARK: Different interests, I guess, different personalities.

She nods.

MARK: And obviously this isn't the way I wanted it to happen, but I'm glad we're spending more time together. I enjoy listening to your stories and having the chance to get to know you better.
MOM: I am too.

They embrace as they never have before.

The day before her move, he takes the train down to San Diego to drive her car up to Los Angeles. As he's backing out of the driveway, he stops so they can take one final look at the home his parents occupied for the previous twenty-five years.

MOM: Your father and I shared many good times here. I'll miss the neighborhood, my friends, but…

She looks over and smiles half-heartedly.

MOM: …life moves on, and you've got to do what you've got to do.

They pull away, leaving years of wonderful memories behind.

* * *

…As traffic slows down in San Juan Capistrano, Mark looks over.

MARK: You doing all right?
MOM: Yeah, I'm okay. I'm fine.

He nods but is still concerned. Along with the flood of memories that are most certainly entering her mind, her health—especially her back—has been poor lately. Two epidural shots have not helped; even the simple act of sitting has now become an issue. She's in constant pain, and she tilts when walking.

MARK: Well, just let me know if you need me to pull over so you can move around for a little while.
MOM: I'll be fine. Thanks.
MARK: Okay.

An hour later, they arrive at Jeff and Teri's house. There are hugs and kisses, and the family does their best to connect just as they have in the past. Mark finds the whole day to be wonderful. The company is great, the food is great, seeing his three nieces is great. He drinks a little more wine than usual to help suppress any thoughts of his dad's passing, but mostly it's a terrific day.

The following morning, he is watching college football when his mom enters the room.

MOM: Hey, I want to talk to you about something.
MARK: Okay, what's up?
MOM: Well, I know you haven't gotten any acting jobs in a while, and I wanted you to know that if you need some money, I can help you. You could go back to school and become a nurse for people who need help in their homes.

?!?

Mark sits still. His head cocks to the side.

MARK: What?
MOM: I saw a commercial for people who do this, and if you need some money—
MARK: Mom, stop it. What are you talking about? You want me to quit acting to do some random job that I have no interest in? One that would take me years of schooling to get into?!
MOM: I'm just concerned.
MARK: Concerned about what?! Do you realize that I work more often than 90% of the people in Hollywood?! Do you know that I'm on hold right now for two other jobs?!! Do you???
MOM: No, I didn't. But if you need any mo—
MARK: Mom! Stop! You're killing me right now!!!

He tries to calm himself but has been so blindsided he can't completely shake it. His face drops into his hands.

MARK: Look, Mom, I love you, but I need you to leave me alone right now.
MOM: Okay, I'm sorry. I just want you to be happy.
MARK: I know you do. Thank you. But I need to be alone right now.

She exits the room.

A thousand times over the years, Mark has questioned himself as to why he continues pursuing an acting career. Now is time for one thousand and *one.*

Why do you do it?... There are definitely easier ways to make money... Has it been worth it?...Oh my god, I can hear my friends now, "I admire you for chasing your dreams."... Yeah, some dreams...All the rejection. Battling day after day to keep your confidence up...No real vacations, no nights out with friends, always trying to figure out how to pay rent…Yeah, some life…And great, now mom wants you to stop…She's never said something like that.

The thoughts and questions run through his mind over and over, but truth is, he knows the answer to the question of why he doesn't stop. It's the same answer thousands of actors have come up with in times of frustration and despair—"What if tomorrow is *the* day?"

The hardest decision an actor has to make is "When do I give up?" Years of toil and disappointment can be vanquished by one perfect audition, one perfect role—*But not if you give up.*

He sits motionless for the next half-hour and contemplates his plan moving forward…*I'm not ready to give up.*

Unfortunately, the incident has put him in a sour mood, and it stays with him for the rest of the day. By 8 o'clock he's mentally beat. He pokes his head in the family room, where Jeff, Teri, and his mom are watching television.

MARK: I'm going to bed. I plan on leaving first thing in the morning, so Mom I need you to be ready.

He begins heading upstairs, where the quiet solitude of an empty room beckons him, just like when he was a kid, but Teri stops him.

TERI: Wait, Mark, is there something wrong? It seems like something's been bothering you all day.
MARK: I'm fine. I just want to go to bed.
TERI: Wait. Come here for a minute. Something's up. Come here and tell us what's wrong.

He can feel his anger building again. As much as he doesn't want to, he broaches the subject.

MARK: You want to tell them?
MOM: I was concerned about his career and I suggested he look into another profession.
MARK: Right. And it makes absolutely no sense.
TERI: Mark, come in here. Talk to us.
MARK: I just want to go to bed. I love you all, but I just want to go to bed. I know me; it's best just to leave me alone. I'll be better in the morning.

He heads to his room and doesn't sleep all night.

The next morning Jeff pulls him aside.

JEFF: Listen, I spoke with mom last night. You know she only has good intentions for you, right?
MARK: Of course.
JEFF: Well, I explained to her it's tough to hear one's mom say, "You aren't succeeding in your career."
MARK: Yeah, that's an understatement.
JEFF: Well, she understands. She's upset that she upset you.
MARK: Okay, thanks. I appreciate you talking to her.
JEFF: No problem. I love you, little brother. You're doing well, keep at it.
MARK: Thanks. I love you too.

They hug, and after saying goodbye to his nieces, Mark grabs his mom's suitcase and loads it in the car. They say nothing during the first ten minutes of the drive. Eventually, she takes the lead.

MOM: Mark, I am so sorry about yesterday.

MARK: It's fine, Mom. I'm sorry I got so mad. I didn't mean to bark at you.
MOM: I just want what's best for you.
MARK: I know. It's fine. Please don't worry about it.
MOM: It's just…I'm just worried that you won't want to talk to me anymore.

His heart drops.

MARK: Oh, Mom, no. I would never stop talking to you. You're my mom. I love you. I will always love you. You've done so much for me; I could never repay you for all that you've done.

He reaches over and puts his hand on top of hers.

MARK: Just do me one favor—
MOM: What's that?
MARK: —Stop saying stupid things.

He looks at her, winks and smiles, and she lets out a relieved, deep laugh.

MOM: I can't make promises.
MARK: This I'm aware of.

Their fingers intertwine. The rest of the ride home is nothing less than enjoyable.

*A week later, Mark finds out he is no longer in the running for the recurring guest star.

Oh well. I guess you'll just have to keep on grinding; keep finding a way to make it work…But I'm still not becoming a nurse.

"WILL YOU BE MY FRIENDS?"

It's a crisp Sunday morning. For the last few hours, Mark has been driving all over the city. First, it was a couple of short trips in the Valley, then a ride out to Hollywood, next it was off to LAX, and finally a drop-off downtown.

As he attempts to make his way out of the area, he notices how busy the streets are. Downtown has continued to grow, and there's more traffic than usual today because the Rams are facing the Philadelphia Eagles at the Coliseum, later in the afternoon.

Before he can completely escape the madness, a request comes in. He maneuvers his car to a high-end hotel, where he picks up a jovial couple.

MARK: Good morning. How are you guys today?
HUSBAND: Great! We've escaped the kids for the weekend!
WIFE: Yeah!!!

The two practically high-five; Mark can't help but laugh at their enthusiasm.

MARK: What? You don't love your kids?
HUSBAND: Ehhhh, they're all right, I guess.

Everyone laughs.

MARK: Where are you two from?
WIFE: San Francisco. We're just doing a little weekend getaway.
MARK: Got it. What are your plans for the day?
HUSBAND: Well, I'm meeting up with some friends; we're going to the Eagles-Rams game...
WIFE: ...Then I'm meeting up with some of my friends while the boys do their thing. We actually have two stops to make. I hope that's all right.
MARK: Oh, a Bieber.
HUSBAND: What?
MARK: Nothing. I'm happy to make both stops.

Over the next ten minutes, they talk about a variety of subjects, including how beneficial Uber has been to Los Angeles.

MARK: No city needed it more. L.A. is so widespread, our public transportation is terrible, and if you ever needed a cab, you had to call forty-five minutes beforehand just to be safe. Now there's someone within five minutes at all times. Plus, Uber's cut down on drunk driving and gives a lot of people, like me, a way to help pay bills. I'd love to be making more money doing it, but I'm definitely glad it's available.
WIFE: Sounds like you're out there grinding.
MARK: Got to. I'm an actor, and like most of us, I've got multiple jobs.
WIFE: Good for you. I always love hearing about people who are pursuing their dreams.

He shrugs.

WIFE: Have you been on any shows that we might have seen?

MARK: Maybe. What do you watch?
WIFE: Okay, let me rephrase that—any specific shows you've really enjoyed being on?
MARK: *Silicon Valley* was a lot of fun.
WIFE: What?! We love that show! What did you play?
MARK: A venture capitalist. Had a small role at the beginning of season two then a big scene at the end of season three. Even got directed by Mike Judge and Alec Berg. It was cool.
HUSBAND: I work up there. I've gotta say, they really nail the characters.
MARK: I've heard that.
WIFE: Well, we'll have to re-watch those episodes and check you out.

Mark shrugs again, and soon the conversation shifts to the Eagles-Rams game. Turns out, the husband went to Stanford and is looking forward to watching Cardinal alum, and Eagles tight end, Zach Ertz.

HUSBAND: The guy is great.
MARK: Yeah, he definitely hurt my Bruins when he was at Stanford. Have you guys always been in the Bay Area?
HUSBAND: Yes and no. We actually just got back. We had been living in the Far East for several years.
MARK: Really?
WIFE: Yep. It's where our kids were born, and we even found our au pairs there. Now they live here with us.
MARK: Cool.
WIFE: (to husband) Speaking of: Did you get them the seats to the Warriors game?
HUSBAND: Yep. Still trying to get the hookup with Steph, but I think it will happen.

Mark's ears perk up.

MARK: Wait "Steph?" As in Steph Curry? *The* Steph Curry? MVP of the NBA, Steph Curry?!
WIFE: Yeah. Our au pairs are huge basketball fans and love him. We're surprising them with some great seats, and we're trying to get them to meet Steph beforehand.
MARK: Wow, I bet they'll be blown away; that's so nice.
HUSBAND: It's fun. We enjoy doing good things for good people, and they have been godsends.
MARK: Man, I have to say, you two are really cool.

They both laugh as Mark pulls up to the husband's drop-off.

MARK: Seriously, though, you're great: down to Earth, friendly. I bet you make great friends.
HUSBAND: Well, you hook that up, honey. I'm gonna go cheer on Zach Ertz and the Eagles. Nice meeting you.
MARK: Nice meeting you too.

The husband exits and the ride continues.

WIFE: So, Mark, what's your story? Wife? Kids?
MARK: Nope and nope.
WIFE: Girlfriend?
MARK: Nope.
WIFE: You want to be set up?

His head tilts.

MARK: You want to set me up?
WIFE: Sure. You seem like a good guy who deserves a good woman. Besides, that's how my husband and I met. I have a soft place in my heart for that type of introduction.

Mark chuckles, thinks about his "issues" for a moment, but grabs one of his photography business cards anyway.

MARK: This is too funny, but sure, why not? Here's my card. My number is on there. Feel free to set me up.

As he hands her the card, he laughs a little harder, realizing just how preposterous the whole idea sounds. Going by their hotel they're staying at, the traveling they've done, and the fact that they have more than one au pair, he's pretty sure his new pals have lots of money. And while they're also plenty cool and don't come across as being egotistical, he assumes their friends run in similar circles.

He imagines one of her pitches.

WIFE: Hey, I've got a great guy for you.
FRIEND: Oh, yeah?!
WIFE: Yep. We met him while we were down in L.A.
FRIEND: Okay, sounds good. Tell me more. How did you meet him?
WIFE: He was our Uber driver.
FRIEND: ——————

He chuckles at the thought...*My new friend, you're gonna have to find a whole new set of gal pals because the present ones will not be around for long.*

She breaks him from his self-deprecating thoughts.

WIFE: Wait a second: You're also a photographer?
MARK: Yep.
WIFE: And this is your website listed on the card?
MARK: Yep.

He hears her tapping on her phone.

WIFE: Mark! Your photography is beautiful!
MARK: Oh, thanks.
WIFE: No, really beautiful. Where are the prices listed?
MARK: Prices? Uh, I don't sell them.
WIFE: Why not?
MARK: I don't know. I just put them up for fun. I only make money by taking actors' headshots.
WIFE: No, you need to do something with *these.*
MARK: Yeah, I guess. I mean, a lot of my friends say I should do a pop-up gallery or something.
WIFE: And?...
MARK: And I tell them "Great, so I should do another type of subjective art where I make no money?" I think the acting thing is enough.

And it's true. While he would love to sell some of his photography, he also knows he could be setting himself up for a whole new line of rejection.

However, his new BFF is having none of his negativity.

WIFE: Oh no, you need to be selling your photography. In fact, I've got a wall I want to redo, and I want to commission your work to fill the space.
MARK: What?! Come on.

The conversation has gotten a little too surreal for Mark; he begins looking for hidden cameras...*Am I being "punked?" Where's Ashton Kutcher? Where - is - Ashton - Kutcher?*

MARK: So, let me get this straight: First, you want to set me up with someone—who I can only assume is going to be amazing—and now you want to buy my photography?
WIFE: Yep. And not only that: I'm going to tell my friends about your work and they're going to want to buy some too.
MARK: Uh…Okay.
WIFE: Is your email address on the website?…Yep, never mind, found it! I'll reach out to you this week; we'll start to figure it all out.
MARK: Uh…Okay.

They arrive at her destination.

WIFE: Bye, Mark. Thanks for the ride. We'll talk soon.
MARK: Uh…Okay.

After she exits, and with no reason to think that Ashton Kutcher is going to pop out at any moment, Mark snorts a satisfied—yet dumbfounded—laugh.

Well, that was different.

*The following week, he gets an email from the wife. They begin corresponding back and forth, discussing various ideas on how to decorate her wall. Just before Christmas, she emails again, letting him know that she'll be in touch in the new year. Unfortunately, it's the last time he ever hears from her.

After finding no new messages in his in-box for the third week in a row, he turns off his computer, snatches his car keys, and heads for the door.

C'est la vie. She's probably too busy searching out a new set of girlfriends anyway.

- 2018 -

"OH, MO! SAY IT AIN'T SO!"

It's a Saturday morning. Mark has found himself in Palos Verdes. The streets are quiet, but he's been busy, and for that he's thankful.

A few weeks prior, he had been traveling on the 134 freeway when traffic came to an abrupt stop. He slammed on the brakes and barely missed striking the car ahead of him. However—while the guy behind him also hit the brakes in time—the next driver did not, leading to a three-car mess. Mark's car was caved in and sat in a body shop all the way through the holidays.

Having had his Uber earnings stripped for weeks, he's now putting in extra hours to make up for lost wages. So far, the day has been profitable, and there's no reason to think things will slow down as a ride request comes in from *Mo.*

Mo money! Mo money!...Eh, that's not funny.

He pulls up to Mo, who is holding bags of groceries that go all the way up to his chin. Mark pops the trunk and hops out.

MARK: Let me help you with those.
MO: Thank you.
MARK: Not a problem.

Sporting a big smile, Mo gets in the backseat, and they're on their way.

MO: Thanks again, and hello! Pretty quick trip. And Happy New Year by the way!
MARK: Thanks, Mo. Happy New Year to you too.

The ride is only estimated to be seven minutes long, which Mark finds to be a shame since Mo is very affable, entertaining, and talkative.

MO: I'm leaving for Russia tomorrow. I work in the oil industry. I go to that part of the world pretty frequently. It's excruciatingly cold.
MARK: Hmmm? Sounds interesting.
MO: It can be. But enough about me. How was your New Year's? Did you drive? Party?
MARK: It was good. Just went to a friend's house. About ten of us. It was cool.
MO: I've heard that drivers can make a lot of money on New Year's.
MARK: Yep. But I got rear-ended on the freeway a few weeks ago; my car was in the shop.
MO: Oh no. Were you all right? No back injuries or anything?

Mark smiles...*Look at my man, Mo! Worrying about his Uber driver and all.*

MARK: Nah. A little sore, a headache for a couple of days, some tightness, but nothing too major.
MO: Well, if you were Mexican you would have had injuries.

!!!!

Mark's smile drops like a bungee jumping hippo. He looks in the rearview mirror...*Seriously, dude?*

MO: I really wish I didn't have to say that.
MARK: I really wish you *wouldn't* have said that.
MO: It's not like I'm racist.

Mark thinks about this for a second. He wants to make sure he didn't miss something...*Nope. I'm pretty sure he just defined being racist.*

Mo, meanwhile, is undeterred by his previous comment.

MO: It's just that the moment anything goes wrong, they're lying in the streets and getting lawyers.

Mark shakes his head...*Wow! Okay, forget about "I'm pretty sure...", He has COMPLETELY defined being racist.*

They pull up to Mo's destination. Mark pops the trunk—he does not get out to help.

MO: Thanks for the ride.

Mark barely lifts his chin in acknowledgement.

As Mo retrieves his groceries, Mark reaches for the app and gives him one star...*I hope you freeze to death on your trip, ya asshole.*

The trunk is shut. Mo taps it, signaling "he's good."

As he pulls away, Mark knows Mo is a lot of things, but *good* is definitely not one of them.

"RUN FOR OFFICE"

It's a midweek day. Mark has just dropped off a passenger in Pacoima, which is located at the north end of the San Fernando Valley and is considered a rough area.

The city is primarily populated by Hispanic families; gangs are part of the fabric of the community. Mark has known people who have lived there for years. He's also had his fair share of drop-offs and pick-ups in the area. What he has come across during these trips is a wide spectrum of feelings towards the city. As with many tough, low-income neighborhoods, people still find it to be home—it's their community; they don't see themselves being anyplace else. Others can't wait to get out. He remembers one of his passengers—a young woman who had just graduated high school—saying, "It's not an easy place to grow up or go to school. There's tension in the air all the time, and kids act up in class. It's just difficult."

At the same time, Mark knows that it only takes a few bad apples to spoil the bunch. His experiences and conversations with people from "bad neighborhoods" have revealed a constant: the great majority of residents in these neighborhoods are wonderful people. They work hard and want the same things in life as anyone else—close-knit families, a house to call their own, a strong, vibrant community—but because of a small faction, their neighborhoods are devalued. Consequently, businesses don't want to invest, and property rates decrease, which leads to less tax revenue and funding for schools. It becomes a domino effect.

As he drives around and waits for his next ride request, he notices a few things: there's an abundance of trash in the gutters, the streets have potholes, weeds are everywhere. He shakes his head... *These daily reminders must be a mental grind, especially for kids.*

The app chimes; it shakes him from his gloomy thoughts. As he gets closer to the pickup location, he spots his passenger, *Jose,* standing patiently on the sidewalk. He's a big guy: 6'2" with broad shoulders. He's more athletic big than weightlifter big, like a guy who played middle linebacker in high school.

Today, however, Jose is not geared up in any kind of athletic uniform; instead, he's wearing long baggy shorts, socks that ride up to just below his knees, and a plain white t-shirt. His hair is cut tight. A few tattoos mark his body. It's as if Central Casting was asked to find a stereotypical Latino gang member and put Jose right there on the sidewalk.

But as always, Mark knows that first looks can be very deceiving; he greets him warmly.

MARK: Hi, Jose. How ya doin'?
JOSE: Good, man. How are you?
MARK: Good, thanks. Let's see where you're heading to.

He swipes and sees they'll be travelling to Moorpark College.

Once he gets his geographical bearings in order and finds his way to the freeway, he continues the conversation.

MARK: What time's your class at?
JOSE: Oh, I'm not going to class. Today's my day off. I'm meeting my wife there. Then we're heading to Ventura to see some family.
MARK: Oh, okay. What do you do for a living?
JOSE: I do maintenance for editing equipment.
MARK: Like Avid machines?
JOSE: Yeah, you know about them?
MARK: I know *of* them. I'm an actor and have some friends who are editors.
JOSE: Got it.
MARK: So how does that work? You get calls when they go down?
JOSE: Sometimes that. Other times, we just bounce around to each of the studios and do maintenance checks.
MARK: Cool. You like it?
JOSE: Yeah, it's a good gig. Being at the studios is cool, and you're at different places all the time, so it doesn't get boring.
MARK: Nice…So, Jose, you look like you may have played some sports in your day.
JOSE: Yeah, a little. You?
MARK: Some basketball in high school.
JOSE: Cool. Where at?
MARK: I went to Birmingham out in Van Nuys.
JOSE: Okay. I know where that's at.
MARK: Did you go to school in Pacoima?
JOSE: Yep.

The conversation is flowing, and Mark is always interested in hearing people's stories, so he jumps in.

MARK: What was it like growing up there?
JOSE: It was just all right, but I got through it.
MARK: Doesn't sound like it was easy.

JOSE: No, it wasn't. There were a lot of bad influences. A lot of my boys got caught up in gangs and died before they were eighteen.
MARK: Oh, wow...If you don't mind me asking: how did you not get caught up in it?
JOSE: Just had to make a choice. One day I was like, "Either make something of your life or die like your boys."
MARK: Did you get flack? Pressured?
JOSE: Oh yeah. I got a lot of that. But you just have to stay true to what you believe in and fight through it. I always tell my nieces and nephews about staying in school, getting a good job, and keeping close to the family.
MARK: You sound like a good uncle.
JOSE: It just is what it is. These kids need positive voices. Where I come from, it's easy to go the wrong direction.

The two settle in for a minute, but Mark can't help himself.

MARK: You're Mexican?
JOSE: Yep.
MARK: What do you think of Trump?
JOSE: Trump is Trump. Don't get me wrong, I think he's an idiot, but I can't worry about him. I need to make sure my nieces and nephews—the kids in the neighborhood—are doing *their* thing. You can worry about what he says, but it's not going to do any good. I'm trying to teach these kids that they need to take responsibility for their own actions and make good choices. Nobody's just going to give them things. They need to know that if they want to have a good life.

Mark nods.

MARK: I gotta tell you, Jose, I think you should run for office someday.

Jose smiles at the idea.

MARK: I'm serious. You've lived the life and know the area; you present your ideas well, and your actions are positive. To me, you sound like a perfect role model and leader. You should seriously do it someday. At least start off with a blog or something.
JOSE: Yeah, I've actually thought about doing a blog.
MARK: Well, I hope you do. I think all communities—not just your own—could use more leaders like yourself.
JOSE: Thanks.

They pull up.

MARK: It was good talking with you. I enjoyed hearing your perspective.
JOSE: Thanks. It was good talking with you too. Also, thanks, man.
MARK: For what?
JOSE: Just being cool. When I got in the car, the way you said "hi," I knew you were cool with me. It was comfortable. Not all drivers are like that.

Mark nods again, remembering that discomfort can strike us all and that words can mean a lot.

JOSE: You have a good day.
MARK: Thanks, Jose. You do the same.

"Great convo and kind."

★★★★★

"GAMESMAN-SHIT!"

Mark has been driving for a few hours. He's in a very good mood. The day before he received confirmation that he will be on another episode of *NCIS Los Angeles*. The news has reduced his stress level considerably. So much so, he's decided to try something new: "The Ride Share Game."

The Ride Share Game begins by having both the Uber and Lyft Apps active then seeing which is surging higher to maximize profits. It's not a complicated game, but he figures if he plays well he'll earn an extra ten or twenty dollars by the end of the night.

After dropping off his latest passenger, he swipes the app, clears his throat, and produces his best game show host voice.

MARK: Leeeeetttttt'sssss play The Ride Share Game!!!

Lyft has a higher surge...*Lyft it is!*

A few moments later, a request comes in to pick up *Steve* at The Huntley Hotel in Santa Monica. A picture of Steve's smiling face pops up on the screen (a benefit of Lyft)...*Looks like a nice guy.*

Mark arrives at the Huntley, and out walks Steve with a cute, younger woman. They hug, Steve heads back to the hotel, and she gets in the car.

MARK: Hi, how are you?
WOMAN: Oooo-kaaaaaay.

While the woman's "okay" drags on for a few seconds, it's no match for the sigh that follows.

WOMAN: *Hhhhhhhhhhhhhhhhhhhhhhhhhh!!!*

What the heck?

WOMAN: Hey, can you turn on some music? There's something about this car—the silence—it's making me not feel so good.

Mark looks in the rearview mirror...*Is she drunk?*

MARK: Um, are you okay?
WOMAN: Yes. Why do you ask?
MARK: Well, you said that silence was making you feel poorly. I've never heard someone say that before.
WOMAN: I'll be fine. Can you just play some music?
MARK: Yeah, um, sure. What would you like?
WOMAN: Oh, anything.

He flips on the radio. K-EARTH is playing the *Go-Go's* hit, "Our Lips Are Sealed." Unfortunately, the lips of the woman in the backseat are not. She immediately begins "singing along" with Belinda Carlisle. None of the words coming out of her mouth are correct, and her voice sounds like someone who has just stepped on a tack, not an *American Idol* contestant.

Mark glances at the app. 53 minutes is the ETA to East Hollywood... *Frick.*

Suddenly, a longer and louder sigh emanates from the backseat.

WOMAN: *HHHHHHHHHhhhhhhhhhhhhhhhhhhhhhh!*

Oh man.

Over the next ten minutes, her sighs increase in length, intensity, and volume; her singing gets worse, and she complements her one-woman band by popping her lips together, blowing air through her cheeks, and smacking her tongue off of the roof of her mouth.

She's the worst beatboxer, ever!

As they stop at a red light, she begins singing a different song than the one playing on the radio. Mark tries to stay calm.

MARK: Excuse me, do you want the radio, or do you want to sing?

She gets the point and stops singing but fills the void by blasting a music video on her phone. Mark shakes his head, turns off the radio, and curses under his breath.

Another sigh echoes throughout the car…37 minutes to go.

The music video finishes; Mark turns the radio back on. He doesn't want any confrontations…*Just get her to her destination.*

34 minutes to go.

Traffic is getting worse. They wind through L.A. like a snake navigating a maze…31 minutes to go.

Then a sound—previously only thought to have been heard in the deepest parts of the Amazon—leaps forward from the backseat.

WOMAN: *AAAAAAwwwwwww-aaaaaaahhhhhh!*

He looks in the rearview mirror. The woman is at the tail end of a prodigious yawn. She slumps in her seat.

A minute later.

WOMAN: *Awwwwwww-Rwaaaaaaaaahhhh!!!*

Are you kidding me?!

Before he can prepare himself, the yawns start pelting him in rapid succession.

WOMAN: *AwwwwwwwwwwFlawwwwbbaaah!!!*
Waaaaaaaahhhaaaaaaaa!!! Blaaaaaaaaaaahhhaaaa!!!

His eyelids clamp down at each stop light... *What is she?—A bear coming out of hibernation?*

WOMAN: *Awwwwww-blaaaaaaahhhhhhhhhh!!!*

As the onslaught continues, sarcastic thoughts begin dancing through Mark's mind...*Ask her if her last name is Berenstain... See if she's from Chicago...Check to see what temperature she likes her porridge.*

He says nothing. He just seethes...24 minutes to go.

Thinking the trip can't get any worse, he soon finds himself sadly mistaken. After each yawn, she begins popping her lips together as if she hasn't had a sip of water in months. Saliva lines connect from her top lip to bottom, and she wriggles in her seat as if crawling towards a life-saving oasis.

Mark's eyes spin like pinwheels…22 minutes to go.

They stop at a red light. Something isn't right…*Wait a second. Wait just one second!*…His eyes dart back and forth…*Oh, my gosh. Oh, my gosh!*

Yes, heaven has rained down upon him. The one-woman-beat-boxing-bear-band is actually not making a sound!…*This is the best thing that has ever happened to me!*

And then it happens.

WOMAN: *AwwwwwBlahblchfAfaawwwwaaaaablllllaaaaa!!!*

It's the mother of all yawns, and he can't take it any longer. He sinks in his seat, grabs a tissue, and waves it above his head in surrender.

WOMAN: I'm sorry, do you think my yawns are fake?!
MARK: No, you just sound like a bear coming out of hibernation.
WOMAN: Hibe—?
MARK: Hibernation! You know, like when a bear sleeps through the winter? *Hibernation!*
WOMAN: Oh. Ha. I get it.

He shakes his head.

WOMAN: I don't know why I'm so tired. I think it's this trip. It's so long.
MARK: The longest ever.

The next twenty minutes are torturous: Yawn, mouth pop, sigh, yawn, air thorough cheeks, yawn, sigh...*At least she stopped singing.*

Mark fantasizes about how to end the trip (it's the only thing keeping him sane).

> **Mark drops off horrible woman. Before she exits the car, he hands her a quarter.**
>
> **WOMAN: What's this?**
> **MARK: A quarter. You won a prize.**
> **WOMAN: For what?**
> **MARK: For being the most obnoxious passenger I've ever had. Now get out!!!**

But he can't find it in his soul to say a thing; he sucks it up until the very end.

WOMAN: Thanks for the ride.
MARK: Mmmmm-hmmmmm.

As she closes the door, his attention shifts to the Lyft App. He glares at Steve's smiling face.

MARK: Next time pick better company to throw in my car, ya friggin' asshat!! One star for you!

He pulls away and turns off the app. But as he drives down the street, trying as quickly as possible to get away from the trollish beast that has been camped in the backseat for the last hour, he can't help but to take a glance in the rearview mirror. There, he sees the woman's image slowly disappearing into a tiny dot. But he swears he still sees her—and hears her—yawn one last time.

AAAAAAAFVAEAAVGGGGGGGGGGGRRRRRRRRSSaa aaaaaaaaaaaaWwwaassbllaaaaaahhhhhhHHHHHHHHH!!!

"Great short ride with a great driver. Thanks."

★★★★★

"LIFE'S 180"

JANUARY 27, 2018

Mark is traveling Northbound on the 101 freeway. Sitting in the passenger seat is an overflowing duffle bag that's filled to the brim with clothes, toiletries, and a bunch of other essentials he'll need for who knows how long. His destination is Thousand Oaks, where his mom is in need.

To say "The previous twenty-four hours have been difficult" would be a gross understatement. There's been numerous phone calls between family members, a trip to the emergency hospital, arguments, even a car accident. At the present time, the details of the previous day are not of any consequence to Mark and only serve as a negative distraction from his most immediate task: take care of his mom and get her to an orthopedic surgery consultation, eight days away.

For months, her back problems have been steadily getting worse, reaching their most severe depths the day before, and leaving the future in doubt. Mark's middle brother has moved out, leaving her by herself, to which she has no complaints.

Being the independent person she is, her plan has been to move from her current residence and into a smaller unit in the same complex. The idea originally seemed to be reasonable, but now borders on highly questionable at best.

As Mark's driving out to stay with her, he is well aware of the formidable situation that's standing in front of him: she cannot live by herself, and with Jeff in San Diego, the onus of taking care of her falls directly on his shoulders.

As he continues driving, he realizes all that needs to be done. The list is daunting. Foremost, is getting her through to the following week so she can meet with the doctor and see if she's even a candidate for surgery. Now eighty-four years old and with high blood pressure, there's a high probability that her body won't be able to handle a major operation.

The thought scares him on many levels. Despite her health issues, his mom has continued to stay very active. She plays bridge twice a week, participates in community discussions, and takes part in two book groups. He knows that if she can no longer make these events, the mental strain, along with her physical liabilities, would quickly take their toll...*I don't even know how long she'd last.*

Along with taking care of her, he also needs to research senior communities and a post-op health care facility with the hope that she is eligible to have an operation. Moving arrangements will need to be made, and her belongings will need to be packed. And there's also his own life to think about; it's the beginning of pilot season—not a good time to take a break. But he has no other choice: his mom needs to be cared for, and he's more than ready to do what he can. It's life's 180: the child now taking care of the parent.

Over the next eight days, he's constantly in touch with Jeff and his cousin, Lori, who is an absolute godsend. Her love, support, and guidance throughout the process are invaluable.

Days are filled with researching senior communities and care facilities, nights are spent packing and throwing away items that will no longer be needed. The discarding of knickknacks, baking pans, and especially her clothes becomes difficult for her.

Each evening, they set aside time to go through the process. Mark pulls out racks of clothes from her closet, then separately holds up each item to see if she wants to keep it or donate it to The Goodwill.

MARK: How about this one?
MOM: Oh, no, I couldn't get rid of that. I wore that when your father and I went to Europe.
MARK: All right, how about this one?
MOM: Oh, no, I couldn't get rid of that. It reminds me of being in Las Vegas with my friends.
MARK: Mom, you've got eighty black blouses, you can't wear all of them.
MOM: Oh yeah, watch me.

They laugh often during these sessions, and he's happy to keep her mind occupied.

Throughout each day, he keeps a watchful eye on her. She can no longer walk further than twenty-five feet without being in excruciating pain. Often times, her whole body convulses as the nerves in her back continually get squeezed between degenerated discs.

She rarely sleeps at night. Mark often wakes to find her sifting through financial records.

MARK: Mom, please stop worrying about all that.
MOM: I'm just not sure how much money—
MARK: Mom, stop. You need to get your rest. Everything will be fine.

One night, he wakes up to hear her releasing some soft groans. Per usual, the light is in on in her room. He gets up to check on her.

MARK: Hey, how are you doing?

She turns to him and smiles. It's a soft, warm smile—almost ethereal.

MOM: I'm dying.

Oh no.

He makes his way to her bed and sits next to her.

MARK: No, no, no, Mom, you're not dying.

He holds her hand, and she caresses his with her other. Her smile continues to shine as she looks lovingly at him.

MOM: No, I'm dying. It's okay.
MARK: Mom, you're not dying. You're just having some problems right now. But we're going to get you to that doctor's appointment, and we'll see what he has to say, okay?
MOM: All right…I love you.
MARK: I love you too.

For the next three hours, they hold hands. She tells him stories about the family and her childhood. She slowly relaxes into the bed. At four-thirty, she finally falls asleep.

A few days later, they meet with the orthopedic surgeon. Jeff has come up from San Diego to help flush out all questions and concerns. Once the consultation has finished, the surgeon feels she is a candidate for an operation called a laminectomy. He believes the procedure will help reduce pressure and she'll be able to walk again without pain. It's a huge relief.

As they drive back to the apartment, Mark knows he still needs to get her through the next nine days when the surgery will take place. Plus, there are still lots of other arrangements to make and work to do. But as they travel west and look into the bright, colorful setting sun, he sees another light that's much more faint. It's the light at the end of a very dark and unforgiving tunnel that's surrounded them during the past week. And while this glint of light is still far, far in the distance, there's no doubt it *is* there.

The next week-and-a-half is difficult, but as they count down the hours, minutes, and seconds until surgery, they keep an eye on that light as a symbol of hope. Together, they make their way towards it.

"MOM"

Mark and his mom are on the 101 freeway, late morning. Traffic is moving pretty well, which is good—not just for obvious reasons—but also because they could both use *anything* to flow their way for a little while.

It's now been eighteen days since he moved in with her, all to get to this day: Surgery Day.

During their stay with one another, the two experienced many bouts of frustration, disappointment, and anger. For the first time in his life, Mark witnessed tears falling from his mother's eyes. It was also the first time that he could control his own.

But despite the hardships they encountered, they also shared loving memories, stories, and plenty of laughs. Many times, they sat next to each other and held hands while talking deep into the night. They watched *Jeopardy* and *Seinfeld* religiously, and Mark left the room whenever *Judge Judy* came on. They had to call the paramedics once, misplaced medications twice, and ate far too many frozen meatballs. But they kept checking in on one another, and when things got difficult, they'd calculate exactly how many hours remained until this day: Surgery Day—a first hurdle that will hopefully lead to physical relief for her and some mental relief for the entire family. They know there's still lots of uncertainty ahead and many other hurdles to clear, but one at a time, and this is the biggest of the bunch.

However, as they travel down the 101 freeway, there is one thing that is quite certain: They know each other a thousand times better than they had just two-and-a-half weeks earlier. They are more at ease in each other's company, and their love and appreciation for one another has never been greater.

MARK: Just three more hours. You're almost there, Momma.

She smiles.

MOM: I don't know how I would have made it to this day without you. I can't thank you enough.
MARK: You're my momma. I'd do anything for you.

Truth is, along with learning a great deal about his mom, he has also learned a great deal about himself. And despite many stressful moments, he wouldn't trade their shared time for anything.

He glances over and sees her smiling in a way that she hasn't in months until—*Quack! Quack! Quack!*—his phone rings loudly through the car's speaker system. She flinches at the fowl noise but quickly calms down, and after a quick conversation with the hospital, he hangs up.

MARK: You know, Mom, if I get you a smartphone, I'm going to set the ringtone to a duck quack.
MOM: Don't you dare. It shakes me up every time.

They smile at the thought.

MOM: Let me ask you something: When you have one of those goober persons in the car and your phone rings, does it make them jump?
MARK: What?
MOM: You know, when you have a goober person in your car.
MARK: Do you mean an *Uber passenger?*
MOM: Yes, Uber, goober. Whatever.

They laugh so hard that Mark nearly slams into the car next to him. Eventually, he collects himself.

MARK: You said "goober person."

They laugh once more before settling into their seats, each of them filled with love. Mom and son. Son and mom.

He looks over at her with respect and loving adoration... *You're all right, Mom. You're all right.*

*The surgery is a success, and it gives her a new lease on life. Within a month, she's walking better than she has in years and without pain.

**She soon moves into a senior community, which is close to both Mark and her niece, Lori, with whom she has a great relationship. For the most part, things work out well. No situation is perfect, and she still has other health issues which pop up now and then, but she settles into her new living arrangement without too many hiccups. The staff is great, she makes new friends, and she even gets healthy enough to drive once more, allowing her to rejoin her bridge game and have wonderful get-togethers with friends.

MARK: Seems like this is working out.

MOM: Yes, it is. You did such a great job watching over me and finding this place. I'll never forget what you've done for me.
MARK: Hey…

She lifts her chin and gazes at her smiling son.

MARK: …*I'll never forget what you've done for me.*

"AND ON YOUR LEFT YOU'LL SEE..."

It's a Tuesday, late morning. Mark has just dropped off a passenger at LAX. He's been driving for a few hours and is ready to go home. He sets the destination option and hopes to get a couple of trips on the way back to the Valley to salvage some gas money.

A request soon comes in from *James*. The directions seem a bit confusing, however—the listed address is on the right, but the GPS is instructing Mark to go to the left...*Oh, Uber.*

He idles in a parking lot for a moment, trying to determine which way to go, when he sees a family of four—two women, a man, and a teenage boy—running across Washington Blvd.

James, a portly man, finds his way into the front seat while the other three jostle for position in the back.

MARK: Sorry about that. The Uber GPS isn't that great.

James answers with a thick (*Thick!*) Scottish accent...*Or is it Irish?*

JAMES: Oh, don't worry, Mark. We found ya. All is well.

The app is swiped. Their destination is a massage parlor in Santa Monica.

MARK: You're all going to go get massages?
JAMES: Oh, no, no. We just want to go to the mall in Santa Monica. But who knows, maybe after.

The whole family laughs and then talk amongst themselves. They're pleasant and cheerful, although Mark occasionally finds it difficult to understand what they're saying due to their accents.

MARK: I'm assuming you're here on vacation. How's it been?
JAMES: Oh, quite nice. We've had a good time.

Everyone in the backseat echoes James' sentiments.

MARK: Where have you visited?
JAMES: Well, let's see: We've been to Venice Beach and the Walk of Fame. Griffith Park…

One of the ladies butts in, but Mark can't understand her.

JAMES: Oh yes, and we visited Compton.
MARK: Wait, um…I'm sorry, did you just say you visited Compton?
JAMES: Yes, my son is a big fan of *NWA*.

The son nods enthusiastically. Mark takes this in for a moment.

He can understand the appreciation for *NWA*, the highly influential rap group that brought the stories of Urban African-American life to the masses through "Gagsta Rap" in the 1980s…*But this kid wasn't even close to being born back then. And I'm not sure the plight of the African American male translates to the streets of Scotland.*

MARK: Let me guess: You saw *Straight Outta Compton?*
TEENAGER: Six times.

Mark laughs.

MARK: Well, I've gotta say: In my couple of years driving for Uber, I've driven many tourists, but I've never heard of anyone going out to Compton.

He laughs a little harder, and everyone in the backseat joins in while James gives details of their excursion.

JAMES: We saw the house that Dr. Dre grew up in, and we got ourselves a wonderful family picture in front of the "Welcome to Compton" sign.

That did it! Mark explodes with laughter. All he can envision is this painfully white family standing on a Compton street corner, posing as if they were taking a group photo with Mickey Mouse at Disneyland.

He eventually stops laughing and James has a question of his own.

JAMES: You ever been out there?
MARK: Oh, yeah. My friend, Joe, is from nearby Lynwood. Back in the day I would go out to his family home for BBQ's. I've also driven a bunch of passengers there.
JAMES: It's not so bad.
MARK: No, it's not. Nothing like you see in the movies or on the news. However, the first time I took a passenger there it was around eleven at night. When I dropped her off she said, "I wouldn't pick up anybody around here if I were you." I got the message. It's not like what you see in the media—gang members on every corner and helicopters constantly flying overhead—but there's obviously some truth to the stories.
JAMES: That's what I mean.

MARK: Right. *Buuuuttttt,* I'm still guessing you guys stood out a little.
JAMES: We did. Especially when we walked into TGI Fridays. Everyone was looking at us like we were lost.

Mark loses it again.

JAMES: Then when we ordered and the waitress heard our accent, she was even more shocked.
MARK: Oh my God, you're killing me.
JAMES: We enjoyed it. It was a good day.

"It was a good day?" Did he just quote, Ice Cube?

They approach the drop-off area.

MARK: Well, folks, it was nice meeting you all. You really made my afternoon.
JAMES: Glad we could help. Take care now.

Mark shakes his head in bemusement and pulls away.

Yep, I'm guessing it's probably just a matter of time before tour buses start circling the infamous streets of Compton.

**"Thank you for your help.
Got a souvenir T-shirt
and a hat!"**

"TIME MACHINE"

It's just past nine in the evening. Mark is struggling to get into his car. Not that he physically can't do it, he's just sick of driving.

A few weeks prior, he was going all out, driving eight hours a day, seven days a week, trying to store up money like a squirrel collecting food for the winter. Acting has been terribly slow—almost two months now without an audition—and he has fallen into "What do I do now?" mode. At the same time, nothing else seems to be going right. Twice over the weekend his mom had to go to the ER. She's feeling much better now, but the weekend—when Mark does most of his driving—was shot, exacerbating his financial situation. Mentally, he's stagnant, and there doesn't appear to be anything in the foreseeable future to shake him from the funk he's in. He's reduced his time in the car in half. Driving for five-hour stretches seems unattainable. In fact, it's now been three days since the last time he's driven...*Need to take those mental breaks here and there.*

But as he views the app and sees that he just recently passed the four-thousand trip marker, he knows that he needs to get out and earn some money. With traffic having died down for the night, he's decides it's a good time to get back in the car.

He turns the ignition key and looks at his lifeless eyes in the mirror...*Just go for as long as you can, even if you only make ten bucks; it's better than nothing.*

A request soon comes in from *Camila*, who's at the ever so popular Porto's Bakery and Cafe... *Who knows? Maybe she'll have some goodies for me.*

When Mark pulls up, a young man gets in the car. He doesn't look like someone named "Camilla" nor is he holding any goodies.

MARK: For Camila?
YOUNG MAN: Yeah. I'm Miguel.
MARK: Hey, Miguel. You just getting off work?
MIGUEL: Yep.
MARK: I was hoping Camila—or yourself—would have a box full of those famous Porto's cheese Danishes and maybe slide one my way.
MIGUEL: Those things are pretty good.
MARK: I live close by, so I pop in now and then to treat myself. I never even liked cheese Danishes, but I was at a party one time and someone had brought a box of them. I was going to pass, but my friend was like, "Just try one." It was unbelievable. I've been hooked ever since. It's basically an addiction.

Miguel chuckles, and the simple sound of laughter helps pull Mark from his depressed state.

He swipes the app and sees that they are heading to Pasadena—twenty-five minutes away.

MARK: So, how long have you worked there?
MIGUEL: About six months.
MARK: You like it?
MIGUEL: Yeah, it's cool. Everyone's nice. It's a good job.

There's a positive tone to Miguel's voice. He seems pleased with where he's at in life.

MARK: Do you have to take Uber to and from work?
MIGUEL: Yeah.
MARK: That sucks. It must take a big cut out of your salary.
MIGUEL: Yeah, it does. But it's okay.
MARK: Sounds like you need to get a car.

The thought of a car brings a big smile to Miguel's face.

MIGUEL: I definitely need a car. I'm saving up for one.
MARK: Good for you.
MIGUEL: I want to get a convertible Ferrari.
MARK: (laughing) A convertible Ferrari? No offense my man, but you may want to start with something a little less pricey. You'd have to work a thousand hours a week at Porto's to even think about that kind of a car.
MIGUEL: Ha! Yeah, I know. But someday I'm gonna get one.
MARK: Well, good for you; keep that eye on the prize. It's always good to have goals.

Miguel nods, then puts on headphones. For the next twenty minutes, neither say a word. A block from his destination, Miguel leans forward.

MIGUEL: Um, excuse me, where are we?
MARK: *Where are we?* Pasadena. Isn't that where you're going?
MIGUEL: No. I live downtown.

Mark shuts his eyes; his sour disposition returns…*I soooo hate this job.*

He pulls over and shows Miguel his phone.

MARK: Well, this is the address that Camila entered.
MIGUEL: Man, I'm so sorry. She must have typed in the wrong place.

Mark's eyes shut again.

MIGUEL: If you drive me home will you get paid for the extra miles?
MARK: I would, but only if Camilla enters the correct address. Can you call her?
MIGUEL: My phone is dead. Can you call her from your phone?
MARK: Sure. What's her number?
MIGUEL: I don't know. I only have it entered in my phone.

Ah, yes, another disadvantage of technology: no one knows anyone's number by heart any longer.

Then Mark has a realization.

MARK: Ya know what? I'm not thinking too well. I can call her through the app.

He presses the phone icon and they wait…and wait…and wait. Camila doesn't answer. The call goes to voicemail.

MIGUEL: Camila, it's Miguel. You put in the wrong address. I need you to enter the right one.

Mark and Miguel look at one another. They know Camila will not be getting the message anytime soon.

MARK: I don't know what to tell you, buddy.

Miguel's head drops.

MIGUEL: I'm really sorry. Can you just take me back to Porto's?
MARK: I can, but you still need to get home.
MIGUEL: Yeah, I know, but I've already wasted enough of your time. You said you live in that area, so at least you'll be closer to home.

Miguel can't look at Mark. His eyes droop like a sad puppy.

Mark sighs.

MARK: I tell ya what: I'm just going to close out the trip and take you to where you live.
MIGUEL: Are you sure?
MARK: Yeah. You need to get home. It's cool.
MIGUEL: Thanks. That's really nice of you.

Mark waves off the thank you.

Twenty minutes later, they arrive in front of Miguel's apartment building. As he exits the car, he reaches into his pocket.

MIGUEL: Here, I've got a couple of dollars. Let me give them to you.
MARK: Don't worry about it. You've worked hard all day. It's not a big deal. Keep it.
MIGUEL: Really?
MARK: Yeah. Just do something nice for someone else down the road. Besides, you need to save up for that Ferrari, right?

Miguel smiles. Mark smiles back.

MIGUEL: I *will* do something nice for someone else. Thanks again.
MARK: You're welcome.

The door is closed. Mark leans forward and knocks his forehead lightly against the top of the steering wheel... *Things have to turn. They have to.*

For the next ten minutes, he sits like a statue. He thinks about his life: where he is, where he'd like to be. He thinks about the disappointment he saw in Chuckie's mom's eyes, months earlier... *Why don't I have lives like my friends? Where did the mistakes happen?*...A few specific incidents immediately come to mind. He begins fantasizing about owning a time machine so he can go back to those moments and reshape his destiny. One particular moment stands out from the rest: Disneyland, junior high graduation trip, Pirates of the Caribbean, sitting in the back of the boat with his crush... *You should have kissed her.*

The memory brings a smile to his face... *Oh well, probably not too many time machines on the market, anyway.*

Realizing the absurdity of his prior thoughts (even if they were just fantasies), he releases a tiny laugh.

You'll just have to try again tomorrow. That's all any of us can do... And who knows? Maybe Miguel will slip you an extra cheese Danish the next time you drop by Porto's.

He laughs a little harder—his soul lifting from the despair that had apprehended his body just moments earlier. Then he has a thought. He checks the time... *Yep, I think you can still make it.*

Twenty-five minutes later, he parks on a quiet, put to bed street. He exits his car and makes his way to a glass front door. He hopes it's not locked. It isn't. He pokes his head in.

MARK: You still open?
VOICE: We are. But before you come in, answer one question for me.
MARK: Shoot.
VOICE: Who was the American League's Most Valuable Player in 1963?
MARK: Elston Howard…How ya doin', Mickey?
MICKEY: I'm doing okay, Mudge. How you doin'?

Mark takes a seat at the counter and grabs a menu. He considers Mickey's question.

MARK: Ya know what?—I'm doing all right…Yeah, doin' all right.

"WHAT THESE EYES HAVE SEEN"

It's a weekday morning. Mark is heading towards Santa Monica after an airport drop-off. The day has been slow, and as he heads North on a predictably jam-packed Lincoln Blvd, he can feel his average hourly wage dropping by the second. He's nearly gotten all the way to the 10 Freeway when, to his relief, the app chimes. Three right turns later, he's at the pick-up spot and waits for *Jackie.*

A message soon pops up on the app—"You will be picking up Steve and his mom—Thanks, Jackie."

A few minutes later, a man appears. He is inching his way down the apartment building's walkway. Mark is a little frustrated by his pace and sees no "mom" either. He rolls down the window.

MARK: Steve?!

The man shakes his head, but as he does so, Mark sees an arm waving behind him. The first man clears, and there's Steve helping his mom down a step. She is moving slowly, and Mark can tell every step is difficult for her. Immediately, he's reminded of his own mom's issues from just months earlier.

As she makes her way towards the car, he gets a better look at her: She's in her mid to late 60s, is using a walker, and has a huge bandage over one of her eyes (although she has the look of someone who has no vision at all).

As she gets closer, Mark realizes that she would have to step over a bumpy lawn to get to his car.

MARK: Would it be better if I moved up a little so she can stay on flat ground?
STEVE: Yeah, just go up to that driveway. Thanks.

Steve helps his mom into the backseat, and once he gets her settled, he puts her walker in the trunk before taking a seat next to her. Mark twists to make sure everyone is buckled in. When he completes his turn, he's met with a pleasant surprise: the woman is smiling from ear to ear.

MOM: Good morning.
MARK: Good morning. How are you today?
MOM: Well, I'll let you know in about a half hour when I see if this surgery did any good or not.
MARK: Oh, okay. Well, I hope it's a success.
MOM: Me too. They're trying something new on me, so we'll see what happens.

Mark already likes his new passenger. She has a great spirit, her smile never leaves her face, and the tone of her voice is upbeat and positive.

MARK: They're trying a new technique on you, huh?
MOM: Yep. I've had all sorts of surgeries on my eyes and nothing has helped. They wanted to give up.
MARK: Oh?

MOM: But I shed some old lady tears, and they said, "Okay, okay, we'll try again."

She releases a joyful laugh and admits that she had put on a bit of an act to convince her doctor to continue exploring ways to help.

MOM: He's a little Italian man; I'm a Southern Baptist, and between the two of us—and God—we came together to give it another try.
MARK: I like it…So, you're from the South, huh? Where about?
MOM: Alabama…Don't hate me for it.

Mark looks in the rearview mirror and sees a little smirk on her face.

MARK: Come on now, I'm sure there's plenty of good people in Alabama. In fact, I had a guy in my car just yesterday from there—he was very nice.
MOM: Oh yes, there are plenty of nice people, but it wasn't the place for me.

Again, her tone never steers towards negativity. As she speaks, she elicits a "this is what life dealt me, better smile through it" attitude.

MARK: When did you come to Los Angeles?
MOM: May 28th, 1971.
MARK: Wow, you've got the date down and everything.
MOM: Well, yes, because May *27th,* 1971 is the day I graduated from high school.
MARK: You left the day after high school?
MOM: Yes. I knew there wasn't anything left for me there, so I took off.
MARK: That's courageous.

She shrugs.

MARK: So, since you graduated high school in 1971, that means you were right there in the middle of it all: in 1960s Alabama.
MOM: Yes, I was. And I saw a lot.

It's hard for Mark to not associate her present eye condition with her last statement—*I saw a lot.* It's as if the injustices she witnessed damaged her eyes.

Over the next ten minutes, she recounts some of her memories.

—She explains how a train track separated the black neighborhoods from the white neighborhoods. How men on the white side of town would patrol the dividing line by driving pickup trucks back and forth while carrying shotguns and nooses and wearing KKK hoods.

—She tells how she saw some boys being pulled from cars and beaten with baseball bats.

—She tells how she and her friends snuck out of their houses one night and saw a group of black men attempt to stand up to the white men, only to see more beatings.

MOM: My mom was so upset with me, but my friends and I had to see if those men would be successful in their demonstration.

She punctuates her recollections with a story about a park in her hometown that only white people could use.

MOM: There was a little train that circled the edge of the grounds. For the longest time, we could only watch that train go around and around. But then they made it legal for black people to be in the park

too. Well, that first day, everyone—and I mean everyone—came to the park to ride that train. And you know what they had done?
MARK: I'm afraid to guess.
MOM: The night before, they went into the park and pulled up the rails, so the train couldn't run any longer.
MARK: Wow.

For the next couple of minutes, no one utters a word. Mark is dumbfounded. Not that he didn't know those were horrible times, but to hear it from someone who *lived the South* in the 1960s, only helps solidify just how disgusting it must have been. He remains silent, but eventually has to ask a question.

MARK: So, I completely understand if you don't want to answer this, but I'm curious: with all that is going on in the world, does it stir up bad memories or feelings?
MOM: Well, let me put it this way: I'm not saying we had come all the way forward, but we had made progress. But then this guy comes into the White House and makes it okay to hate again.

Mark nods and looks in the rearview mirror. What he sees is an amazing woman, sitting tall and proud. A strong woman indeed: still full of life and having seen plenty of it.

They arrive at the doctor's office. Mark retrieves the walker out of the trunk while Steve helps his mom from the car. Mark comes around to her. He puts his hand on her shoulder.

MARK: Good luck today, and thanks for telling me about your life. I appreciate you.

She smiles beautifully.

MOM: You're welcome. You have yourself a great day.

Mark smiles as he watches them walk away.

I will have a great day, ma'am, I have no excuses not to.

"DR. JEKYLL AND MRS. JIVE"

It's an early Saturday morning. The sun is breaking through the haze, streets are quiet. Mark heads towards Valley Village to pick up *Richard* for his first trip of the day.

He arrives at the pick-up destination, waits for a moment, then sees a man and woman exit a modest condominium. They are—as famous college basketball announcer, Dick Vitale, would say—*an M&M.* They are a *MisMatch.* Richard, late 40s, is an average-looking guy at best. He's wearing sweatpants and a ratty t-shirt. Meanwhile, his companion is stunning and much younger than he. Also, despite the early hours, she's dressed to the nines as if on her way to an elegant party. She strides towards the car with a regal air about her...*I shall call you Elizabeth*...Richard, on the other hand, has slumped shoulders, and his feet slide forward like he's forging through thick mud.

Even in a city where ordinary guys often end up with beautiful women, the combination of these two doesn't seem right...*This is an M&M at the highest level.*

Mark's confusion only grows when both get in the car. He assumed Richard had ordered Elizabeth the Uber, was walking her out, and would say goodbye at the curb. But now, as the two are buckling up, he can't even imagine where they could be going, especially in such opposite states of dress.

Richard's voice shakes Mark from his befuddled state.

RICHARD: Good morning. Do you mind taking an extra little trip? The first stop is just a few blocks away.
MARK: Sure. Just direct me to where we're going.
RICHARD: No problem.

Richard navigates for the next five minutes, intermittently talking with Elizabeth. Their conversation recounts a dinner party from the previous evening. Elizabeth is very articulate and continues to impress Mark with her overall aura. When given the chance, he takes a peek at her in the rearview mirror…*Man, she's gorgeous…* But he's still confused as to her relationship with Richard…*They can't be a couple, can they?*

RICHARD: Just make a left into that parking lot.
MARK: Where Bank of America is?
RICHARD: Yep.

They pull in. Richard jumps out and heads to the ATM. As he does so, Mark slyly takes a few more glances at Elizabeth…*My goodness, she's amazing.*

Richard hops back in the car.

RICHARD: Thanks. Can you just drop me off at my place and then take her home?
MARK: Um, sure.

The whole situation is still a little odd *until* Richard hands Elizabeth the stack of cash that was just withdrawn.

Ah, ha!!!

As he backs out of the parking spot, Mark hears Elizabeth counting the money.

RICHARD: Don't worry; it's the right amount.

Yes, now it all makes sense. Going by her well-spoken manner and classy attire, Mark figures Elizabeth works as a *GFE*—as in *Girlfriend Experience*—where men hire educated, worldly, and classy women to be their "date" for the evening. The whole idea is to give the customer the feeling of being on an actual date before the likelihood of sex at the end of the night.

During his time as an Uber driver, Mark has had his share of passengers from the sex industry. And, like all passengers, their personalities landed all over the spectrum. His encounters have also brought about a wide range of emotions from within himself: he's found himself surprised, saddened, and frequently intrigued…*I wonder how they got to this place in their life?*

—There was the two conservatively dressed, college-aged women who began their trip by discussing the merits of Kurt Vonnegut and Charles Dickens. At no point did Mark expect one of them to be an exotic dancer, but as their conversation drifted from literature to work, it became quite clear that one worked at a gentlemen's club. The first reveal was when she mentioned her shift beginning at eight and finishing at four in the morning…*Ain't nothin' open at 4 AM but CVS pharmacies, late night diners, and strip clubs*…And if Mark wasn't 100% sure at that point, when she described the good looking professional men who would arrive at the beginning of the night and expected extra "favors" for free, it was the nail in the coffin.

—There was the worn out, overly made up, pale, and emaciated woman he picked up at 5:30 in the morning outside a Hollywood strip club. When she entered the car, she asked Mark to roll down the window because she didn't feel well. After obliging, he listened to her phone conversation as she described the night's events to a friend. There had been a fight, she slapped a customer for touching her during a lap dance; she took multiple whisky shots in a bathroom stall with two other dancers, and her phone case was smashed somewhere along the way. As she spoke, Mark noticed how weathered her voice sounded. Her slumped over, lifeless posture, mirrored her tone. As they neared her destination, she asked her friend if she had any whiskey—apparently her night/morning was just getting started. Mark couldn't help but feel depressed as he watched her drag herself out of the car, knowing that this was probably a typical night for the young lady, with no indications that her life would soon change.

—There was the 5'6" guy who was on his way to the airport. Five minutes into the ride, he mentioned that he was a porn star and was off to visit his girlfriend in Florida, who was also in the business. During the forty-minute trip, he described the industry's politics, relationships, and highs and lows. Surprisingly, the framework sounded no different to Mark than any other passenger's stories about work-related politics, relationships, and highs and lows.

—And finally, there was the call girl who thought Mark was cute. He had picked her up just a few blocks from his apartment and was driving her to see a client at an LAX hotel. She flirted with him throughout the ride, including taking guesses at his "dimensions". Her forward ways, of course, made him anxious. As they pulled up to the hotel, she took it a step further by asking him if he wanted to take her back home—*really take her back home*—instead of dropping her off. As he turned to her and contemplated the proposal, he couldn't help but find humor in the situation and his life...*Ya know, buddy, the last person you saw who was even semi-naked was George Wendt. Perhaps, you shouldn't pass on this*...In his mind he could hear a handful of his friends—both men and women—whispering in his ear, "Have fun, relax, enjoy yourself." But in the end, he declined the invite.

...As he pulls up to Richard's condo, he flashes back to the hotel call girl...*I wonder what I would have done if she had been as amazing as Elizabeth?*

Richard begins exiting the car.

RICHARD: It was great seeing you. We'll do it again soon.
ELIZABETH: I had a lovely evening. I look forward to it.

He shuts the door and Mark sneaks another peek...*Now don't you get all flirty with me, Elizabeth. I might have to squash all my morals if you do.*

For the time being, his morality is safe as she shifts her focus to her cellphone...*That's right: Don't even think about glancing at the cute Uber driver up front, you'll immediately fall in love*...She dials, then puts the phone to her ear, making even such a simple action look stylish and glamorous...*My God, she's so classy, so beautiful, so well spoken, so....*

ELIZABETH: Guuuuuuurrrrrrrrlllllllllllllll, whatchoo doin'?

!!!

...Well, 2 out of 3 ain't bad.

Mark quickly looks in the rearview mirror just to make sure it's still the same woman in his car. And indeed, it is her! Her transformation has him dumbfounded, intrigued, *and* flabbergasted. He believes the greatest thespian in the City of Los Angeles is in his presence! It's as if a switch was flipped the moment Richard stepped out of earshot, and the lovely lady gracing the backseat transformed herself from "Elizabeth" to "Lizzy from the Block" at the speed of light. He wants to pull over and give her a standing ovation for the performance she has given Richard... *Well done, Lizzy from the Block! Well done!!!*

While still stupefied by what he's just witnessed, he merges onto the 101 freeway when from out of nowhere five police cars speed past. They pull over a car, block the freeway, and draw their guns.

LIZZY: Guurrrrrrrlllllll!!! You wouldn't believe what I'm seein' rightch here!!! There are cops and guns and a whole lotta mess!!! I'm like duckin' for cover!!!

Mark grabs his phone and opens up the Facebook App. He updates his status... *You wouldn't believe my day so far.*

Five minutes later, the suspect is apprehended, traffic is reopened, and Mark finishes taking Lizzy home.

As they head down her street, she points to a modern high-rise in the center of Hollywood.

LIZZY: Rightch over there.

He parks.

LIZZY: Thank you so much. You have yourself a good day.
MARK: Thanks. You too.

She starts to get out of the car, but suddenly—and to both of their surprise—he halts her.

MARK: Hey, wait a second.

She stops and turns to him.

MARK: I wanna tell you something.
LIZZY: Yes, what's that?

He pauses for a moment. Then, with all his might, he tries to excavate some long-lost courage—courage that's been buried inside of him since he was six years old.

MARK: Um…You're very beautiful.
LIZZY: Awwww, thank you. You drive safe now.

As the door is closed, he looks down at his hand—it's still. He smiles.

See? That wasn't so difficult…Still glad she didn't flirt, though.

He takes a moment to watch Lizzy saunter towards the high rise—her movements still teeming with class. She reaches the entrance and looks back to the car for the briefest of moments. She grins innocently, then disappears behind the frosted glass front doors.

Au revoir, Lizzy from the Block. Au revoir.

"ur kinda hot in a dad kinda way actually"

★★★★★

"JACK"

It's a Thursday. Mark is trying his best to be productive. His first order of business is calling his Congressman to express a few concerns...*I don't know if it will do any good, but at least you're trying.*

He spends the rest of the morning sending out emails to casting directors and uploading a new reel to various casting websites. It's now been fifteen months since he's booked a role on a show: the longest drought he's had in years. 2018 has not been kind. Other than doing the second episode of *NCIS LA* and booking a Hyundai commercial, there's been nothing. He realizes the first half of the year was basically a wash as he tried to get things in order for his mom, but now it's episodic season—the busiest time of the year—and auditions are still slow. His acting friends concur—they haven't had many auditions either—but "misery loves company" isn't helping. It's been five years since the last time he seriously thought about giving up acting, but with his slump gnawing on him daily, he's just about ready to walk that tight rope again and is wondering if falling off for good would be for the best...*Just let it go. You gave it your all. Open up a photography studio and make that your full-time pursuit.*

But no matter how much he encourages himself to find another path, he still can't commit to it. After all, who knows if the next day is *the* day. He looks at himself in the mirror and half-heartedly tries to convince himself that continuing is the best option… *You can reassess after pilot season.*

Feeling that he's accomplished what he had set out to do in the day's early hours, he calls his mom to see if she'd like to get together for lunch. She tells him that she's feeling weak and dizzy.

MARK: Did you eat this morning?
MOM: Yes, but I didn't sleep well last night.

She never sleeps well, so making a point of it probably means she only slept for an hour or two.

MARK: Well, I called to see if you wanted to have lunch, but if you're not feeling up to it maybe you should just get some rest. I can come by and sit with you if you'd like. It's up to you.
MOM: No, lunch would be nice. It's fine.
MARK: All right. I'll be by in a couple of hours. See if you can get in a nap in the meantime.
MOM: Okay. I'll see you in a little bit.

He hangs up and soon receives an email from his managers; a few residual checks have come in… *Good. I can grab them after lunch.*

A couple of hours later, he picks up his mom.

MOM: Can I pay this time?
MARK: Nope.
MOM: I'm worried about your money.
MARK: You're always worried about my money. I could win the lottery and you'd be worried about my money. I'm fine. In fact, there are a couple of checks waiting for me at my manager's office. I'm going to pick them up this afternoon.

MOM: Oh, good. Okay.

As they eat, she describes some shenanigans taking place at the senior community where she lives.

MOM: It's like high school: cliques, one person's mad at this person, another's mad at that person, people sleeping together.
MARK: Yeah, I've noticed a couple of guys checking you out.

She blushes.

MOM: There are one or two who *do* seem to have a little crush on me.
MARK: Uh-oh. Don't you make me have to go in there and set things straight.

She laughs and seems to be feeling a little better.

MOM: Can you believe that shooting the other night in Thousand Oaks?
MARK: Twelve dead. It's so sad.
MOM: I don't know what people are thinking.
MARK: Neither do I. Sure would be nice to have some sane gun control laws.
MOM: Hopefully, the mid-term results will help.

Now it's Mark's turn to feel weak and dizzy.

Like countless others, the last two years have taken a lot out of him. The current administration's policies and rhetoric have left him confounded and have caused him to sever many long-standing friendships due to extreme ideological differences. What may be even worse is his constant battle with himself, wondering if he's living up to his father's standards.

MARK: Well, I'm not sure that we got the "blue wave" everyone was hoping for, but getting the House will help, and I'm excited about all the young, new representatives.
MOM: I think your father would be happy.

He smiles at the thought.

By the time they get back to her room, her energy has increased. He hangs out for another half-hour before excusing himself with one final, long hug.

MOM: Don't worry about me. I'm feeling much better. You can go.
MARK: Usually, people say they're feeling better as soon as I *do* leave, not before.

She giggles.

MOM: Love you.
MARK: I love you too.

He kisses her cheek and is off to see his managers.

Despite his acting career hitting a speed bump, he still loves the team he has. Mariko, Hank, and Lily are all thoughtful, positive, and hardworking. Plus, he knows he needs to do his job as well… *Gotta book some roles, Bloom. Only so much they can do.*

At the very least, visiting Hank and Lily always lifts his spirits. Not only are they fun to be around, but he feels he can voice his thoughts and concerns whenever the need arises. This day is no different. They discuss ideas on how to improve his career and remind him that acting is a roller coaster ride and to keep grinding. Their words are helpful.

MARK: Thanks, guys.
LILY: Of course. It's what we're here for.
HANK: You keep at it, Bloomin' Onion. Bookings are coming soon.

By the time he gets to his car, it's already four in the afternoon and traffic has built up. Driving back home from Mid-Wilshire doesn't seem too prudent, so he prompts the Uber App.

After taking his first passenger on a quick trip into Beverly Hills, another request comes in with a newly implemented notification: The trip is estimated to be over 45 minutes long. While longer trips bring in more money, they're not as beneficial during rush hour since the mileage rate is much higher than the minutes rate. Being stuck in traffic is like spinning one's wheels without spinning one's wheels.

He looks closer at the request…*No surge, huh? Forget it. Probably just a terrible trip to LAX.*

He declines the request, but it doesn't take long for another to come in. There's still no surge attached, but he figures it's better to take a short trip than nothing at all.

As he approaches, he sees his passenger, *Jack*: 70-ish, in good shape, and sporting an enormous, bushy mustache. A small duffle bag is flipped over his shoulder.

He takes a seat, closes the door, and smiles.

JACK: Hey there, Mark. LAX, please.

Nooooo.

Mark swipes. The estimated time is exactly *45 minutes*. He sighs.

JACK You okay?
MARK: Yeah, it's just that the app is supposed to let us know when a trip is forty-five minutes or longer.
JACK: Well, aren't longer trips better?
MARK: Well…

He explains the pros and cons.

MARK: It's certainly not your fault. To the airport we go.

Jack releases a robust laugh.

JACK: Well, good; I wouldn't want my driver to be mad at me for the next hour.

He laughs again, and Mark joins him.

MARK: Where are you heading to?
JACK: Back home to Ohio.
MARK: What were you doing out here?
JACK: I was visiting my daughter and my newest grandson.
MARK: That's exciting.
JACK: Yes, it is. It was the first time I got to hold him. It was wonderful. It gave me so much hope.
MARK: That's fantastic. How many grandkids do you have?
JACK: Ten. Four children. Ten grandkids.
MARK: Whoa!

JACK: How about you? You got any kids?
MARK: Ah, no. Never seemed to work out.
JIM: You've still got time.
MARK: Yeah, maybe. But I figure if it hasn't happened yet, it's probably not going to. Besides, I've got more issues than a box of tissues.

Jack releases another monstrous laugh.

JACK: Do you do anything else other than drive for Uber?

Mark would prefer to avoid the subject—he'd much rather hear about Jack's family—but he relents.

MARK: I'm an actor.
JACK: Well, that's fantastic.
MARK: Eh, it has its moments. Unfortunately, I'm in a big slump right now. Can't seem to book any jobs.
JACK: I'm sure it will turn around.
MARK: Yeah, I hope so. What about you? What kind of work have you done?
JACK: Well, I did several things when I was young then I followed my dreams and made a living as a musician.
MARK: Nice.
JACK: Yeah, those were some amazing times: being up on stage, the audience is grooving off what you're doing. There's no feeling like that. You ever get that kind of experience?
MARK: Yeah, back when I was doing stand-up. Getting a room full of people to laugh was an amazing rush.
JACK: So, you do understand.

Mark nods.

JACK: Yep, I lived in that world for a long while, but then a lot of that life started catching up to me. One night, I was playing at this small club. In between sets, I was sitting at the bar—drunk and stoned—when I looked to my right. Sitting next to me was this pathetic guy: worn out, just a mess.
MARK: Yeah?
JACK: Yeah. But then I realized no one was sitting next to me. I was looking in a mirror.
MARK: Whoa! Whoa!

Jack laughs at the memory.

JACK: I saw what I had become and was sickened by it. You ever have that happen?

Mark let's out a tiny laugh.

MARK: Well, it's not quite the same—nor as dramatic—but one time at the gym, I turned my head and thought I was looking at some dude. And I was like, "Look at this guy over here!"
JACK: "Look at this guy over here!" "Look at this guy over here!" That's hilarious!!

Mark agrees and soon they are both laughing at their reflective moments.

JACK: Yeah, sometimes you get a glimpse of yourself and you're not happy with what you see.
MARK: What happened after that night at the bar?
JACK: I got out of the music world. Found a desk job for the next twenty years. For me, it was time.

Jack smiles at his recollections. Then his voice quiets.

JACK: Ya know, you go through life and the years just pass on by. You might struggle for a lot of that time, and when you look at what the future holds, it can be scary. But then from out of the blue, something happens, and it gives you hope. That's why holding my new grandson was so special: It gave me hope. You see, my daughter has had a tough time.
MARK: Yeah?
JACK: Yeah—she's an addict, and my grandson was born addicted. But now he's out of *NICU*, and I got to hold him. It gave me hope.

Mark looks in the rearview mirror and sees Jack smiling. The opportunity to hold his grandson appears to have lifted a load of bricks from his shoulders.

MARK: What's going to happen moving forward?
JACK: Well, my daughter's in-laws are going to take care of the baby for a bit while she and the father go to rehab...And then we'll see. But I have hope.

His smile broadens. It's a wonderful smile: one constructed over time by a lifetime of experiences—both good and bad.

As the ride continues, the two converse about a variety of subjects, but each topic eventually funnels right back to the same theme: *the journey of life*. They talk about instinctual moments and joyous moments and even sorrowful ones.

MARK: Reminds me of that famous Jim Valvano quote: "If you laugh, you think, and you cry, that's a full day. That's a heck of a day."
JACK: I like that. And it's true. We each have our own paths and unique experiences, and when they're all woven together, they make up the tapestry that represents our time on the planet.

As they close in on LAX, Jack inquires further about Mark's acting career. Being that he's in a much better mood than he had been at the beginning of the trip, he's more willing to open up.

MARK: I enjoy it. Just wish it was more consistent.
JACK: Do you have a favorite acting experience?
MARK: Well, I had a great time being in an independent film a couple of years back, but a long time ago I did something else.
JACK: What was that?
MARK: It was a one-man show that I put up called *Tales From An Empty Bedroom.* It was something I was very proud of. I wrote it, produced it, and performed it. And other than a couple of friends who gave me some critiques and pointers, I had no director. I just wanted to put it up.
JACK: That's fantastic. What was it about?

Mark explains that from an actual childhood event, he became a dreamer.

MARK: …And where does one dream best?—Alone in his or her empty bedroom.
JACK: Okay.
MARK: But over the course of the show, I'd start to lose control of the dreams, which then led to different characters and stories.

Jack smiles.

JACK: Well, that sounds fascinating. You should be proud.
MARK: Thanks. I guess I need to remind myself of those accomplishments every once in a while.
JACK: Absolutely…Do you still write?
MARK: Here and there. Actually, I recently started making a compilation of the people I've met as an Uber driver.

JACK: That sounds great.
MARK: It's been interesting, that's for sure. You come across such a wide range of people and often become privy to people's journeys. It makes you realize that we all have strengths and weaknesses, good days and bad, moments we wish we could take back and others where we surprise ourselves by what we bring to the world.
JACK: I bet you have some interesting tales.
MARK: Some. But it's more about people and all the little snippets of life I come across. That's what truly fascinates me.
JACK: Any ride jump out at you?
MARK: Yep. One will always stick with me more than the others.

Mark tells Jack about *Toni,* the woman whose son had been killed, and how they held hands at the end of the hour-and-a-half trip.

Tears begin to well up in his eyes. He wipes them away.

MARK: Sorry about that. I get emotional whenever I think about it. I've always been like this.
JACK: No need to apologize. That's what life is all about: those interactions that come out of nowhere. You were really there for her.
MARK: I guess. It's just...I just don't like being so sensitive.
JACK: Why?
MARK: It just makes me feel like I'm not tough enough. Like I'm weak.
JACK: Hmmmm?...Did you ever think it could be a sign of strength?

Mark's eyebrows furrow.

MARK: What do you mean?
JACK: Well, being sensitive isn't only an internal quality, it's also external. It makes you aware of the needs and emotions of those

around you—you're sensitive *to* them. That allows you to be compassionate, giving, and a good person…In my eyes, that's a strength, not a weakness.
MARK: Wow, um…I guess I've never thought about it that way. Thanks, Jack.

Jack smiles and enthusiastically claps his hands together.

JACK: Well, if you ask me, I think you need to write that book. I'm going to tell my wife about it, and I want to read it someday.

Mark grins at the thought.

They pull up to the terminal.

MARK: Jack, it was a real pleasure. I wish you and your family nothing but the best.
JACK: It was a pleasure indeed, Mark. Just remember: When things get tough, there's always hope around the corner.
MARK: I'll remember that. Thanks.

They firmly shake hands, and Jack starts to exit, but just before he closes the door he pokes his head back in.

JACK: Oh, and what else are you going to do?—
MARK: I'm going to write that book. I will.

Jack winks. Mark smiles.

JACK: You take care, now.
MARK: Thanks, Jack. You too.

The door is shut.

Mark pulls away and begins to zig-zag through LAX traffic. Soon, the app chimes and—for quite possibly the first time—the sound brings a smile to his face. Memories of different rides start flowing into his mind. He recounts all the interesting people he's met: the stories, the laughs, the deep conversations. He realizes that many of his most memorable interactions came about with people from vastly different backgrounds than his and how fortunate he was to have gotten a glimpse into each of their lives...*Thanks again, Jack.*

As he continues to review the encounters, another realization comes into focus. His mind travels back to one of his first passengers: Carissa. He thinks about how she had cried throughout the ride and how difficult it was for him to find the right words to soothe her.

He keeps walking down his mind's road...*But, later, you knew what to say to help ease Toni and Kyle's pain during their troubled times.*

Further recognition comes forward...*You didn't worry about looking foolish when you performed your spoken word piece for Yazmin or when you bared your soul to Keira...You ventured out. Saw different parts of the city. Met new people...You listened and learned, taught and grew...Heck, you've even started writing again.*

He closes his eyes and soaks it all in, well aware of what's happened... *It's been subtle, but it's been happening all along.*

His eyes reopen, and he smiles bigger than he ever has before... *You've changed. You've actually changed.*

A moment later, I pulled up to the curb, stepped out of the car, and began looking for *Will.* I couldn't find him at first, but then a young man broke through the airport crowd.

ME: Will?
WILL: Yeah, hi. I hope you weren't waiting long.
ME: Not at all.
WILL: Cool. Thanks for picking me up.
ME: No problem.

I grabbed his luggage, loaded it into the trunk, and we got in the car…Will opted to sit in the front seat.

ME: So, how's your day going?
WILL: I gotta tell you, Mark, this has been one of the most interesting twenty-four hours of my life.
ME: Yeah? Well, it looks like we've got a forty-minute trip ahead of us, so tell me about it.
WILL: Okay. Well, it all started yesterday when I was leaving my house. My neighbor…

The End…
and the Beginning…

ACKNOWLEDGEMENTS

Writing this book has been a ride in itself. Somehow, a simple Facebook post about a woman needing a ride from Pacific Coast Highway, blossomed into a full-blown manuscript.

Who knew?...Well, plenty of people, actually.

From the jump, many friends encouraged me to continue writing the stories of my Uber adventures and the people I met along the way. At times, recounting those trips was fun; other times, it led to great displeasure and frustration. (I now respect writers so much more than I ever did before.) I want to thank everyone who pushed me to keep moving forward. I never could have gotten to this point without your words.

A handful of people went to even greater lengths.

Along the way, there were multiple drafts. Each time I completed a new one, I'd distribute it to a handful of friends. In return, I was given pages upon pages of notes—both positive and negative. While I didn't always agree with the critiques—and found it fascinating and extremely exasperating when one friend hated a particular story while another found the same tale to be one of their favorites—the notes were always valuable. More importantly, they had "care" behind them. I can't thank these people enough for the effort and love they gave me. David, Kim, Maria, Tamara,

Alan, Liz, Greg, Renee, J.D., and Jordan, you will always have my thanks. I appreciate you.

Also, special thanks to Lisa, Katy, and Sean for their guidance and talents.

Finally, to all of the passengers I met along the way: What an interesting bunch you all are (I write that as a compliment). Thank you for allowing me to see a glimpse of your lives. Your uniqueness is a blessing. Many of you gave me reason to pause and think. I learned a lot from our conversations, and I truly believe I have grown as a person from our interactions.

I'd like to finish by paraphrasing the words of my father during his final moments; words we should all be reminded of from time to time: Be kind, compassionate, giving, and let's take care of the planet.

Thanks again.

Peace.

Made in the USA
San Bernardino,
CA

58981624R10210